# SOME *Truth with Maps:* *A Primer on Symbolization and Design*

**Alan M. MacEachren**
Department of Geography
The Pennsylvania State University
University Park, PA 16802

document production **Jillaine Thacher**
illustrations **Catherine Reeves and Jillaine Thacher**
Deasy GeoGraphics Laboratory
**David DiBiase**, Director
The Pennsylvania State University

**Association of American Geographers**
**1710 16th Street**
**Washington, D.C. 20009-3198**

Library of Congress Card Number
ISBN 0-89291-214-6

**Library of Congress Cataloging in Publication Data**

***Publication Supported by the AAG***

*to my Mother*
*for her continued support*

# CONTENTS

## Foreword

One important outcome of the development and increasingly widespread use of geographic information systems and computer mapping software is that many individuals with little or no formal experience in cartographic design are now engaged in mapmaking. In an earlier era, when someone who wanted to present geographic data but did not have the skills or equipment to draft and reproduce a map turned to the professional cartographer, the cartographer would manage the design and production process to make an acceptable map. The products of some of the original computer software for making maps were often discounted by professional cartographers because they did not measure up to accepted standards of cartographic design even though they may have provided some measure of satisfaction to the software users.

If computer-based cartography had remained experimental and limited, the shortcomings of the software packages and their applications might have been ignored. Because the ability to produce maps using computers is so common and because cartographic display remains a major method for the analysis and presentation of geographic data, the search for ways to improve maps and mapmaking must continue. Poorly designed maps can inadvertently miscommunicate information on the nature and arrangement of geographic objects. The history of cartography also offers examples of the use of maps as powerful instruments of propaganda designed to distort truth intentionally.

SOME *Truth with Maps: A Primer on Symbolization and Design* is an effort to share the knowledge base of cartography with readers who are making maps using the current computer-based technology or using maps produced with it. As the author states, this publication is not an attempt to replicate an introductory cartography text. Instead, the monograph offers an exposition of the critical components to be considered when making a map for the task at hand.

The Association of American Geographers is pleased to publish a monograph addressing these concerns for anyone whose understanding of cartographic design could be strengthened. We hope that this volume will educate geographers and others who collect, analyze, and map geographic information to produce better maps and to develop more powerful software for modelling the world we explore.

Ellen K. Cromley
Robert G. Cromley
Co-editors

## Preface

Understanding how to design and use maps produced by geographic information systems (GIS) is critical to the analysis and policy decisions that these systems are intended to support. The purpose of SOME *Truth with Maps: A Primer on Symbolization and Design* is to introduce existing and potential users of computer-mapping and GIS software to cartographic symbolization and design issues, problems, and approaches.

If spatial patterns and associations in environmental and social data are to be discovered, meaningful questions asked, and appropriate policies formulated, analysts and GIS project managers require the most complete possible understanding of the available data. Maps are an ideal means to provide a synthesis of that data, but many analysts who now have access to mapping tools have not been trained in map symbolization and design.

This Primer provides an introduction to mapping principles with an emphasis on maps used in the context of environmental research, policy formulation, monitoring, and management. It does not include a comprehensive description of all aspects of cartographic symbolization and design. That is what current texts provide. SOME *Truth with Maps* details a process for systematically considering cartographic symbolization and design issues so that scientists and/or policy analysts will be equipped to deal with the inevitably unique mapping problems with which they are faced in the course of their activities. Fundamental issues and principles are stressed and examples are used liberally to demonstrate how those principles might be applied. Existing cartographic texts treat map symbolization and design from the narrow perspective of "presentation graphics." This Primer, in contrast, addresses a more complete range of applications from data exploration by environmental scientists, through policy formation by Program Managers, to presentations at public meetings.†

†*This publication was prepared in cooperation with, and partially funded by, the National GIS Program in the Office of Information and Resource Management (OIRM) of the U.S. Environmental Protection Agency. I would like to acknowledge their support (particularly that of Tommy Dewald and Dave Rejeski) and extend appreciation for permission to incorporate EPA examples in this volume.*

## Cover Illustrations

The front cover includes a map of Chesapeake Bay representing dissolved inorganic nitrogen. Excess nitrogen in the Bay (along with other pollutants) has resulted in drastic decreases in the productivity of the overall ecosystem. The map depicted is one example from an interactive reliability visualization environment (RVIS) being developed in the Geography Department at Penn State. The goal of RVIS is to analyze space-time trends in water quality for the Bay and simultaneously consider the certainty or uncertainty of information being used to assess the trends.[†]

The cover map depicts nitrogen with a continuous tone color scheme that emphasizes the ordered nature of nitrogen concentration data. The scheme represents low data values with light red and high data values with dark red. Specifically, color value is changed from the bottom of the scale to the midpoint, then color saturation is decreased in the high end of the scale (see Chapter 2 and Chapter 5 for information on color terminology and color choice for maps).

One goal of the research effort from which the nitrogen map is taken is to develop tools for representing uncertainty in map display. The map on the back of the cover offers one simple way to represent uncertainty inherent in the nitrogen map. The front map is based on a standard distance-weighted interpolation of dissolved inorganic nitrogen values collected at the 49 sample sites used in the long-term EPA monitoring effort for the Bay. It is immediately clear that the sampling density is not high and that some sections of the Bay are more adequately sampled than others. See Chapter 4 for additional ideas on visualization quality and the representation of uncertainty.

---

[†] *See MacEachren, et al. in 1993 for details of the RVIS system. Much of the programming for the initial RVIS prototype was done by David Howard. Among other things, he designed the color palette used for the cover map and figured out how to export the maps for inclusion on the cover. His assistance is appreciated. The RVIS research effort from which the cover illustrations are sampled was originally stimulated by the NCGIA Visualization of Data Quality Challenge. I would like to acknowledge their role in facilitating data acquisition and that of the U. S. Environmental Protection Agency who provided the data. Appreciation is also extended to the Earth System Science Center at Penn State for access to and assistance with the Interactive Display Language (IDL), the development platform for RVIS.*

# 1

# The Roles of Maps

*This chapter provides an overview of the range of map uses in geographic analysis and decision making and suggests ways in which the specific use and user of a map are critical to proper symbolization and design choices. The abstractness of maps, with the inherent pluses and minus that abstraction implies, is emphasized.*

What is a map? What are maps for? When asked these questions, what comes to mind? For many people, the prototypical map is a highway map with the prototypical use being to facilitate travel from here to there. For others, a topo sheet is the first choice that comes to mind. Again, the typical use conceived of might be as a travel aid (for those who like to hike), or as a planning tool that allows delineation of drainage basins or provides a base upon which potential highway locations can be plotted. In all of these roles, the map is primarily a presentation device. It presents an abstract view of some portion of the world with an emphasis on selected features such as roads or terrain. When most map users, even trained cartographers, approach the task of map symbolization and design, they typically assume a presentation goal for which a single map must be selected. This leads to questions about how to generate the *optimal map* for the task at hand.

The goal of producing an optimal map is not equally applicable to all maps. David DiBiase (1990) recently developed a graphic model of the range of uses to which maps and other graphics might be put in scientific research (Figure 1.01, page 2). This basic model is relevant, not only to science, but to applied geographical analysis and spatial decision making with a GIS. In this graphic depiction of the role of maps and graphics, we see that presentation is at one extreme of a range of map applications from exploratory data sifting in search of patterns that should be investigated to the presentation of data analysis results or of a plan for cleaning up a toxic spill. The concept of selecting an optimal map, although possibly relevant for presentation, becomes less relevant (and perhaps even counter-productive) as we approach the exploration end of the continuum.

In DiBiase's model, a critical distinction is made between "visual thinking" and "visual communication." Maps can be used for both, but the goals of symbolization and design will differ. For visual thinking, maps are tools that can prompt insight, reveal patterns in data, and highlight anomalies. The goal is to help us notice something, such as a relationship between the location of industry and incidence of health problems in a population. Symbolization and design decisions made by the map author must facilitate our ability to notice the unexpected. In contrast to this pattern seeking goal, the goal of visual communication is to make a point, to communicate what we think we know. If a comprehensive analysis using maps, health records, statistics, modeling, etc. convinces you that there is a link between the geographic distribution of particular pollutants and a specific form of cancer, then a map can be designed

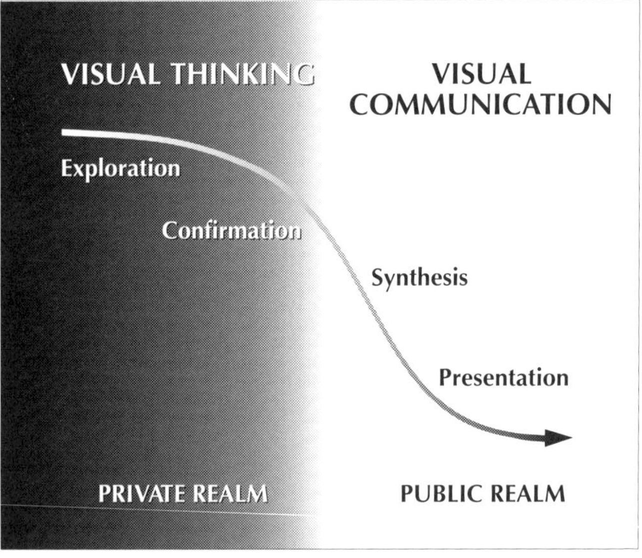


***Figure 1.01*** *The functions of graphics in the research sequence. From the investigator's point of view, graphics change from reasoning tools to communication tools as an investigation expands from a private to a public endeavor. The downward slope of the curve suggests the hypothesis that visual thinking involves higher-order cognitive tasks (for the investigator) than does visual communication. Reproduced with permission from DiBiase (1990),* ***Earth and Mineral Sciences****, Bulletin of the College of Earth and Mineral Sciences, The Pennsylvania State University.*

to communicate this conclusion to the person formulating long term policy decisions.

Visual thinking and communication are not mutually exclusive map goals, but rather two ends of a continuum along which gradually changing goals lead (or should lead) to differences in design and symbolization. At the visual thinking end of the continuum, for example, the map already has the analyst's attention. There is less need for visual "hooks" that draw a reader to the illustration. In the middle of a long report, however, such hooks, in the form of dramatic colors, high contrast, iconic symbols, drop shadows, etc. may serve an important role in drawing enough attention to the map for it to have an impact.

In the four sections that follow, examples are provided of map-based exploration, confirmation, synthesis, and presentation. To provide continuity, all examples deal with environmental issues.

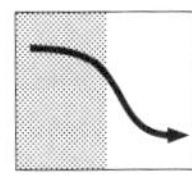

## Exploration

Early in any investigation that involves the use of GIS to manipulate and examine spatial data, maps can be a particularly important exploratory tool. Maps and graphics at this stage often go undocumented because they remain in the private realm of an individual researcher or small group of researchers. The representations used are often schematic and generally not considered to be of "publishable" quality. One such exploratory mapping endeavor that was not intended for a publication or report is described in a book chapter on visualization in geographic research. The relevant passage is quoted below (MacEachren, et al. 1992, p. 105-106):

> *A fascinating example of the process of exploratory visualization at work was provided by a group of colleagues. As a part of an evolving research effort dealing with issues of global climate, Dan Leathers, Brent Yarnal, and Michael Palecki produced a choropleth map*[1]*, originally hand drawn with colored pencils, depicting correlations between U.S. winter temperatures and the Pacific North American (PNA) teleconnection, a zonal index of the mid-tropospheric circulation over North America (Figure 1.02, page 4).*

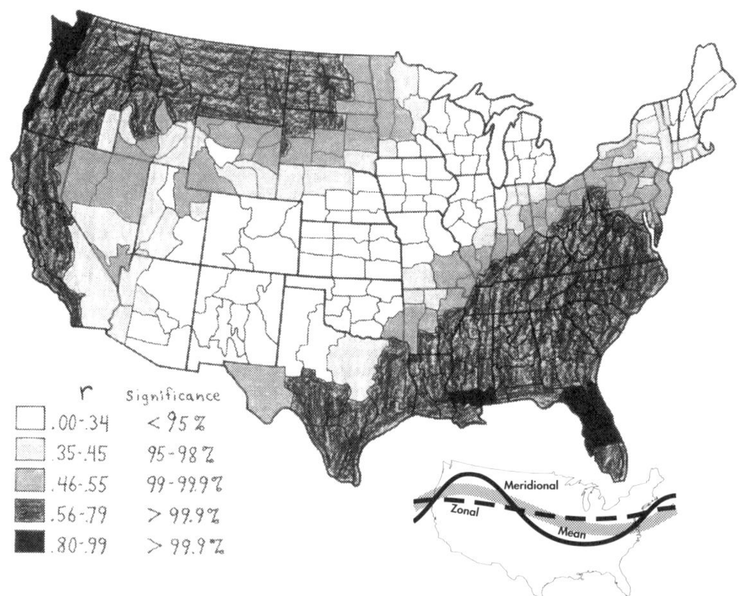


*Figure 1.02* *Correlation between the Pacfic North American teleconnection index and mean winter U.S. temperature. This choropleth map (the original was hand drawn using colored pencils) represents values for each of the 344 climatic divisions of the conterminous U.S. The inset illustrates the mean position of the tropospheric flow in comparison to meridional and zonal flows (represented by positive and negative PNA indices, respectively).*

*The map presented an intriguing and unexpected pattern. A high PNA index indicates the presence of a "deep, strong Aleutian low extending from the surface to the upper troposphere in the north-eastern Pacific, an upper level anticyclone centered over western Canada and a deeper than normal upper level trough located over the south-central United States" (Yarnal and Diaz (1986: 197-198)). Negative values on the index indicate absence of this pattern, that is a jet stream with no dominant troughs or ridges. The choropleth map demonstrated a strong correlation between the PNA index and temperature for both the Northwestern and the Southeastern U.S., with the Northwest being warmer than normal and the Southeast cooler.*

*In trying to explain this pattern, the researchers considered several possible explanations and connections to global circulation patterns. Going against the conventional wisdom that strong PNA patterns are a winter phenomenon and have little relationship to weather during other seasons, they found a similar relationship between the PNA index and temperature on an annual basis. A comparable relationship was identified for precipitation. Once discovered, the relationship was determined to have a strong physical basis, with topography exerting a blocking influence that reduces the association for the diagonal band from the Great Lakes to the Southwest. Working from the initial discovery, Leathers, Yarnal, and Palecki produced a series of maps, did some numerical analysis, and eventually demonstrated links among strong PNA patterns, El Niño events (warmer than normal ocean temperatures in the eastern Pacific), and polar circulation patterns. Their findings have significant implications for long-term weather prediction as well as for the regional impact of changes in global climate.*

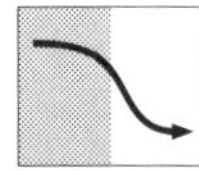

## Confirmation

As an environmental investigation progresses, assumptions are made, questions are posed, and hypotheses are generated. Maps and other visualization tools at this stage of investigation are often used as a way to confirm initial suspicions. Separately or in combination with other graphics they can show the outcome of a modeling effort, or draw attention to anomalies by combining or transforming the original observations. These graphic expressions all play a role in confirming or countering hypotheses that have been posed. It is often the visual display of anomalies or residuals (cases that remain unexplained when a dependent variable is regressed against one or more independent variables) that leads to the greatest insights.

One interesting example of a confirmatory use of map based graphics that turned up an unexpected relationship is provided in a video produced by the Deasy GeoGraphics Laboratory at Penn State University (DiBiase, et al. 1991). The video uses animated maps and graphics to explore the results of predictions of various global climate models (GCMs) about climate change and its impact on Mexico. The video was designed to support research by Liverman and O'Brien (1991) dealing with reliability of model estimates and what it means for agricultural planning in marginal areas.

Most results of GCM analysis have suggested that temperatures will increase if atmospheric $CO_2$ were to double. An animated map was produced on which histograms linked to thirteen Mexican cities showed means and variances for five different GCM predictions of temperature and precipitation throughout a year. It was clear from the animation that all models predict increases in temperature for a $2xCO_2$ scenario. The predicted increases are not just for the overall mean, but for every individual station. By itself, this result is a confirmation of expectations concerning global warming. In spite of this apparent confirmation, however, uncertainty is evident when the GCMs are compared. It is immediately clear that the models differ from one another, that these differences vary through the year, and that among-model variation is quite high during selected months.

To get a more complete picture of these model differences, data for individual cities were reexpressed.[2] The reexpression, in the form of reordering of the data, is used to focus directly on intra-model variability. Temperature data for Puebla were reexpressed by transforming data from a chronological sequence to a sequence ordered from months in which model predictions agree most closely to months with high among-model variation (Figure 1.03). To enhance the important feature of this reexpression (the variability or uncertainty among models), duration of each scene in the animation was controlled by the among-model variability (i.e., scene duration increased as among-model differences increased). What resulted was a clear picture of highest disagreement (or

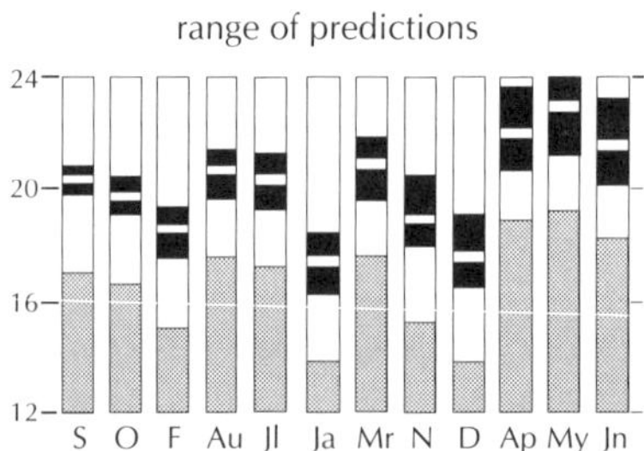


***Figure 1.03*** *This set of figures compares predicted and observed temperatures for Puebla, Mexico. The gray bar represents monthly mean observed temperatures. The black zone symbolizes the range of five GCM predictions for a two-times-$CO_2$ scenario. The white line across this zone is the mean of the model predictions. The scenes are ordered from months in which predictions vary the least to those varying the most.*

greatest uncertainty) in the model predictions during the spring planting season — exactly when the greatest certainty is required. This planting season uncertainty had not been noticed until data were reexpressed for this animation. In this application, therefore, the multiple views of data undertaken as part of the confirmatory stage of analysis leads to the conclusion that current GCMs may be unreliable (or differ substantially in their reliability) for making estimates concerning potential impacts of increased atmospheric $CO_2$ on agriculture in marginal areas.

Maps and other graphics can depict both patterns and anomalies, but are subject to their own data processing uncertainties. As a result, maps can mislead a user into seeing patterns that are not there, or missing patterns that are (see Chapter 4). Maps, therefore, can only be one part of a confirmatory stage of data analysis in which various analytical tools are brought to bear on the problem at hand.

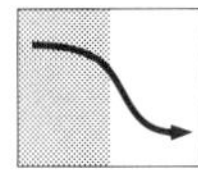

## Synthesis

As an analyst gains confidence in a perspective on an environmental issue, maps provide a tool through which ideas can be synthesized. They allow the analyst to produce a coherent, but abstract statement concerning patterns and relationships being uncovered. Each stage in data processing and display represents a process of abstraction. Key features from the next lower level of analysis are highlighted and local details, random noise, etc. are filtered away in an effort to get at the essence of a situation. The goal of synthesis is to make up for the lost detail by gaining perspective (i.e., stepping back from the data and the specifics to the point where the "big picture" becomes apparent). Synthesis is an activity in which an expert makes informed decisions about what to emphasize, what to suppress, and which relationships to show.

A typical example of a map produced at this stage of analysis can be found in the recent EPA Region 6 Comparative Risk Project Ecological Report (EPA 1990b). For this project, a team of investigators used GIS and modeling techniques to evaluate "the residual risk posed from 22 environmental problem areas identified by EPA Headquarters and the Regional Comparative Risk Project (RCRP) directors" (EPA 1990b, p. 1). For 15 of the 22 problems, there was sufficient potential risk in Region 6 and sufficient data to carry out a complete evaluation. Using a mathematical model, an ecological risk index was calculated for each of these 15 problems and individual maps were prepared (Figure 1.04). These individual maps can be used in exploratory analysis to look for geographic patterns and anomalies. For example, it is apparent that ecological risk due to ozone and CO is particularly high along the Gulf Coast of Texas, but much of the Louisiana Gulf Coast is at only moderate risk.

A basic type of cartographic synthesis is used by the authors of the Ecological Report to address the overall implications of the 15 individual risks. An aggregate, or cumulative ecological risk index is calculated by summing the individual risks for each ecoregion. The resulting map dramatically demonstrates the high ecological risk along the entire Gulf Coast and Mississippi River Valley, and the gradual decline in risk from the east to the west of the region (Figure 1.05). This synthesis is, of course, only one of many data/map syntheses that might be used to summarize the analysis. Different maps would result, for example, if the individual risks were not treated as equally serious (as unweighted summing of index values assumes). In addition, spatial filtering of the indi-

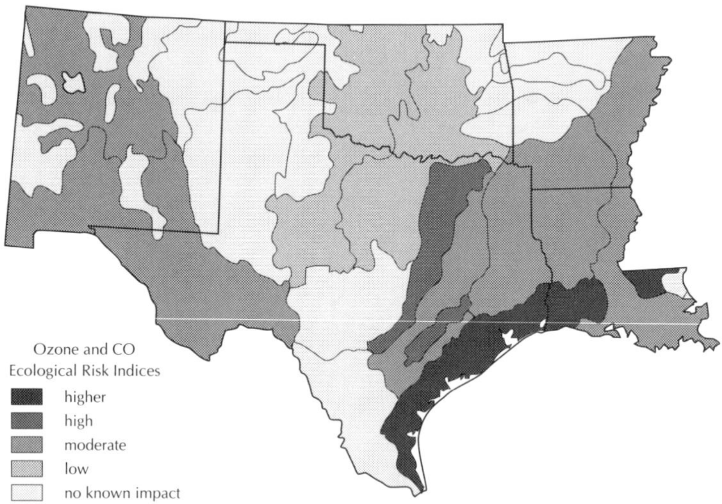


***Figure 1.04*** *Map of ecological risk due to ozone and CO for EPA Region 6. After map 10 in Region 6 Comparitive Risk Project Ecological Report (EPA 1990b).*

vidual values might be used to account for interrelations among the adjacent ecoregions (i.e., spatial autocorrelation) or to filter out the impact of fixed ecoregion boundaries when considering phenomena that recognize no bounds (e.g., toxic air pollutants).

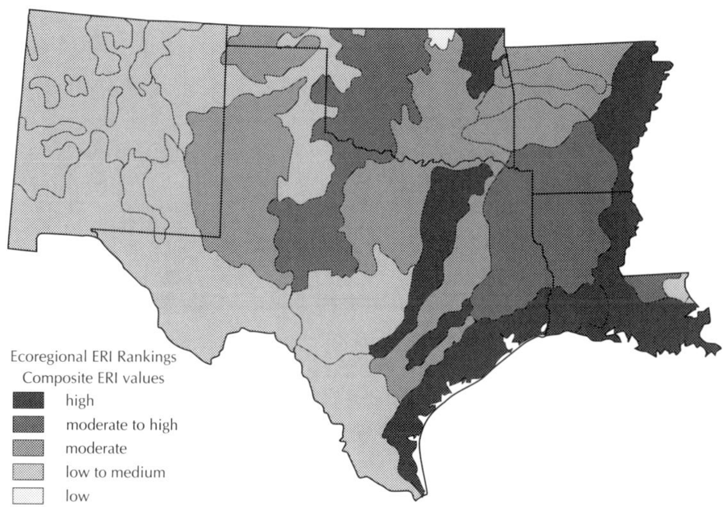


***Figure 1.05*** *Ecoregional ERI rankings map that depicts the cumulative risk due to the 15 environmental risks assessed for region 6. After map 17 in Region 6 Comparitive Risk Project Ecological Report (EPA 1990b).*

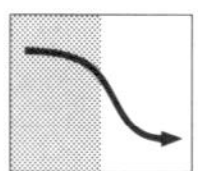

## Presentation

Once you are convinced of a location (e.g., of toxic waste), an attribute at a location (e.g., alkalinity of surface water), or a relationship (e.g., between an industry and a health hazard) and you want to convince someone else of your assessment, a map is an ideal presentation device. A well designed map is convincing because it implies authenticity. People believe maps. It is this general acceptance of maps (in contrast to suspicion of statistical analysis) that makes maps a powerful presentation device, but one that must be constructed and used with care[3].

An outstanding presentational map was developed at the U.S. EPA by Omernik and Powers (1983) to illustrate the regional patterns of mean alkalinity of surface water in the conterminous U.S. (Figure

1.06). "The map was developed from mean annual total alkalinity values of approximately 2,500 streams and lakes and from the apparent relationships of these data with land use and other macro-watershed characteristics, such as soil type and geology" (Omernik and Powers 1983, p. 133). Like the EPA Region 6 aggregate risk map discussed above, Omernik and Power's alkalinity map could be considered a synthesis. They, in fact, state that the map combines measurement and expert knowledge in ways similar to that used to fill in detail of precipitation patterns in areas of scarce data. Once they were satisfied with their synthesis, however, they moved on to the presentational stage. The emphasis on presentation is apparent in the goals they identify for the map and by its publication as a map supplement in a major geographic journal.

The authors cite three specific goals for their map: (1) provide a national perspective on the extent of the problem, (2) provide logic or rationale for selecting geographic areas for more detailed studies, and (3) allow more accurate regional economic assessments of acid-precipitation impacts on aquatic resources. Specifically, the map is intended to provide a picture of the sensitivity of water to acidification. Sensitivity (as indicated by alkalinity) is partitioned into six categories. Care was taken when selecting category breaks

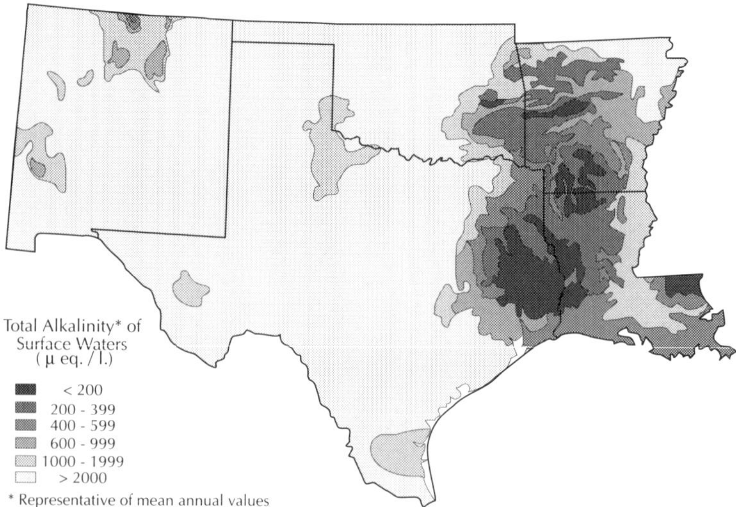


***Figure 1.06*** *Reduced scale reproduction of the EPA Region 6 portion of Total Alkalinity of Surface Waters (Omernik 1982). Original map used area fills of reddish-brown through orange to yellow.*

to avoid depicting either a worst-case or a best-case condition (see Chapter 3 for a detailed discussion of issues on data classification). As the authors state, their intent was "to show what one might expect to find in most surface waters most of the time" (Omernik and Powers 1983, p.133). For analysis, particularly if working at a more local scale, the worst- and best-case scenarios might prove valuable in planning responses to environmental disasters. The middle ground, however, is more appropriate for a presentational graphic intended to guide broad national scale policy formulation.

## Summary

In this chapter, a model of the role of maps and graphics in geographic analysis and decision-making is presented. This model suggests a distinction between maps as visual thinking tools (used in early exploration of data sets and confirmation of patterns noticed) and maps as visual communication tools (that facilitate synthesis and presentation of results and conclusions). This distinction is particularly critical to design and symbolization of maps in a GIS environment because GIS provides tools that facilitate multiple views of data and flexible map design/symbolization choices. Although some design and symbolization principles apply consistently across the entire exploration to presentation spectrum, the difference in goals (i.e., noticing the unexpected versus communicating the known) requires different strategies. In the next section, the fundamentals of a cartographic language system that underlies these flexible goals are introduced.

### Endnotes

[1]*A choropleth map depicts quantities aggregated to a set of contiguous units (e.g., counties, census tracts, etc.) by shading the area of each unit to correspond to a value range that the unit's aggregate value falls within.*

[2]*For a detailed explanation of the concept of reexpression applied to space-time mappings, see DiBiase, et al. (1992).*

[3]*For discussion of the negative consequences of this general acceptance of truth and objectivity in maps see Harley (1989), Monmonier (1991a), and Wood (1992).*

# 2

# Cartographic Language

*In addition to location in space, a limited set of graphic variables is available with which to build a map: symbol size, shape, pattern (texture, orientation, and arrangement), color (hue, value, and saturation), and focus. Data to be mapped can be at a categorical (nominal or ordinal) or numerical (discrete or continuous) level of measurement and can be treated as being either positional, linear, areal, or volumetric. A good map designer knows how to match graphic variables with these spatial dimensions and measurement levels in effective ways.*

Maps consist of relatively abstract marks on paper, a computer monitor, or some other display medium. We are able to make sense of those marks if we know the graphic (i.e., cartographic) language, just as we are able to interpret groups of letters from the alphabet if we know the written language.[1] Like written language, cartographic language depends upon the context in which the fundamental marks appear. Unlike English, or other written languages, however, there are often no prior agreements about the definition of basic symbols (words) in particular contexts. For maps, kind and amount of contrast among often arbitrary marks, rather than preset definitions of words, is the key factor in defining the language. Definitions of map marks (i.e., symbols) are generally not fixed, but provided with the map in the form of a legend. Because symbols can change their meanings at the whim of a cartographer, a key step to making maps intelligible is to match the kind of contrast between and among symbols to the kind of contrast among the things represented. This is a first step toward achieving appropriate symbol-referent relationships, a topic of Chapter 3.

## Spatial Dimensionality

In developing the cartographic language through which any particular map will speak, there are three interrelated issues which must be considered: the spatial dimensions of the features mapped, the level of measurement at which data are collected, and the graphic primitives (and their variations) that will be used to represent the features. Cartographers, since the 1950s, have categorized data and the phenomena they represent according to their spatial dimensionality. Four categories can be identified: positional, linear, areal, and volumetric. Similarly, map symbols have also been categorized as point, line, area, and volume symbols. A logical cartographic language would match symbol dimensions directly with phenomenon dimensions. Following this logic, a point feature on a map (e.g., a point pollution source) would be represented with a point symbol (e.g., a black dot). It might at first seem that a sound cartographic language would have the equivalent of a grammatical rule that would make these symbol-feature matches mandatory. The problem with such a strict formulation of cartographic language is that the categories of phenomena identified are scale dependent and subjectively interpreted. A city, for example, is a point in a world atlas, but might cover an entire sheet on a 1:24,000 topographic map (Figure 2.01). Similarly, rivers can be interpreted as lines at one scale or for one purpose, but be areas for other scales or purposes (Figure 2.02).

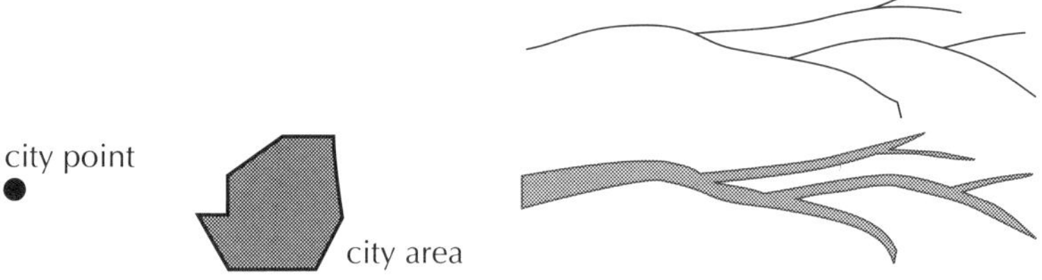


***Figure 2.01*** *A city as point and area.*

***Figure 2.02*** *A river as line and area.*

For clearly defined physical features, the choice between point and area, or line and area, is often dictated by the map's scale (e.g., it is impractical to attempt showing the areal extent of the Mississippi River on a page sized map of the U.S.). Often, the decision is more subjective and the map maker's choice will have a substantial influence on the interpretation of the map. For example, on a map showing the bounds of the health hazard zone around a nuclear power plant in the event of an accident, treating the boundary as a line (represented with a linear symbol) rather than as a transitional area (represented by an area — possibly with indistinct edges) will give the impression of a certain versus an uncertain location (Figure 2.03).

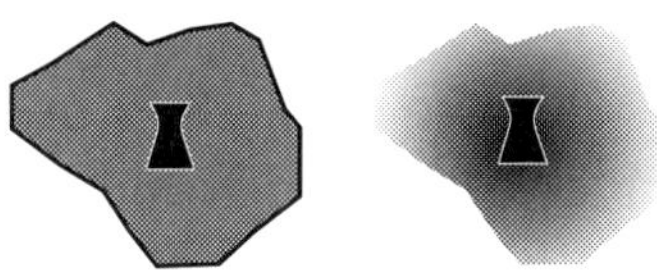

***Figure 2.03*** *A health risk boundary as a distinct edge versus the same boundary as a fuzzy-edged area to emphasize its imprecision and transitional nature.*

## Level of Measurement

Once the spatial dimensionality of the phenomena to be represented is determined, the next step in working out the language of a particular map or map set is to determine the level of measurement at which data are obtained. This is important, as will be seen shortly, because different graphic primitives are effective in communicating data differences at each level of measurement. Levels of measurement are usually divided into numerical versus categorical. For categorical data, two sub-categories are also usually distinguished: nominal and ordinal. Nominal distinctions are distinctions in kind of thing (e.g., air pollutants might include CO, ozone, lead, etc.). There is no natural or implied order among nominally differentiated data. Ordinal data, as the label suggests, have an implied order or sequence (but no numerically defined difference between positions in that order). The categories that appear on many opinion surveys provide a typical example of ordinal data (e.g., high, medium, and low environmental risk or strongly favor, favor, uncertain, against, or strongly against increased federal taxes to finance the Superfund cleanup effort). At a higher level of measurement are numerical data which, in addition to being ordered, have quantities assigned to the steps in that order. Within the numerical level, a further distinction is usually made between continuous and discrete values (or real and integer in terms of computer processing). Continuous data can in principle take any value within a relevant range of variation (e.g., CO concentration in the atmosphere can be recorded with any desired level of precision that available instruments are capable of). Discrete data, on the other hand, can take only a limited number of numerical values from a predefined set (e.g., the number of deaths from lung cancer in a particular population can only be specified from the set of non-negative integer values).

## Graphic Variables

After determining the spatial dimensionality and the level of measurement of data to be depicted, the map maker is ready to consider how the available variations in graphic primitives are to be matched to the variations in the phenomena, or the data that represent them. At the presentational end of our map use continuum, it is particularly important to match variation in phenomena and variation in graphic symbols in an intuitive way so that the map's language is easily translated by an unpredictable range of map users. For the other end of the continuum, exploratory maps, there is usually a single analyst or small team who are highly knowledgeable about the features depicted. For exploratory applications when noticing the unexpected is a primary goal, achieving visual contrast is at least as important as creating visual logic. Even here, however, illogical matching of graphic symbol dimensions and data dimensions may impede the analyst's ability to notice patterns that were not already anticipated.

One of the first comprehensive attempts to create a typology of graphic variables and their suitable uses was presented by Bertin (1983) a French cartographer/information designer.[2] He identified x-y location in the plane, size, value, color, texture, orientation, and shape as the available graphic variables and provided detailed guidelines about the kinds of variation that each was best suited to represent. Building from Bertin's original formulation and incorporating modifications suggested by McCleary (1983), Morrison (1984), and others, an expanded set of graphic variables has been developed (DiBiase, et al. 1991).[3] The set includes: location in space (the x-y-z dimensions), size, shape, color value, color hue, color saturation, texture, orientation, arrangement, and focus. This set of graphic variables is not necessarily a comprehensive list. It seems, however, to include the fundamental units from which all other static variables can be built. These variables, therefore, serve as the building blocks from which most map symbolization can be derived.

Each of the graphic variables can be applied to each of the spatial dimensionality categories described in Figure 2.04. We can combine color hue with area symbols, for example, to create an ecoregion map in which different hues are used to visually differentiate the ecoregions. The graphic variables can be matched on a more limited basis with the levels of measurement described above. For example, some variables (e.g., size) provide intuitively obvious indications of numerical distinctions, while others (e.g., shape) do not.

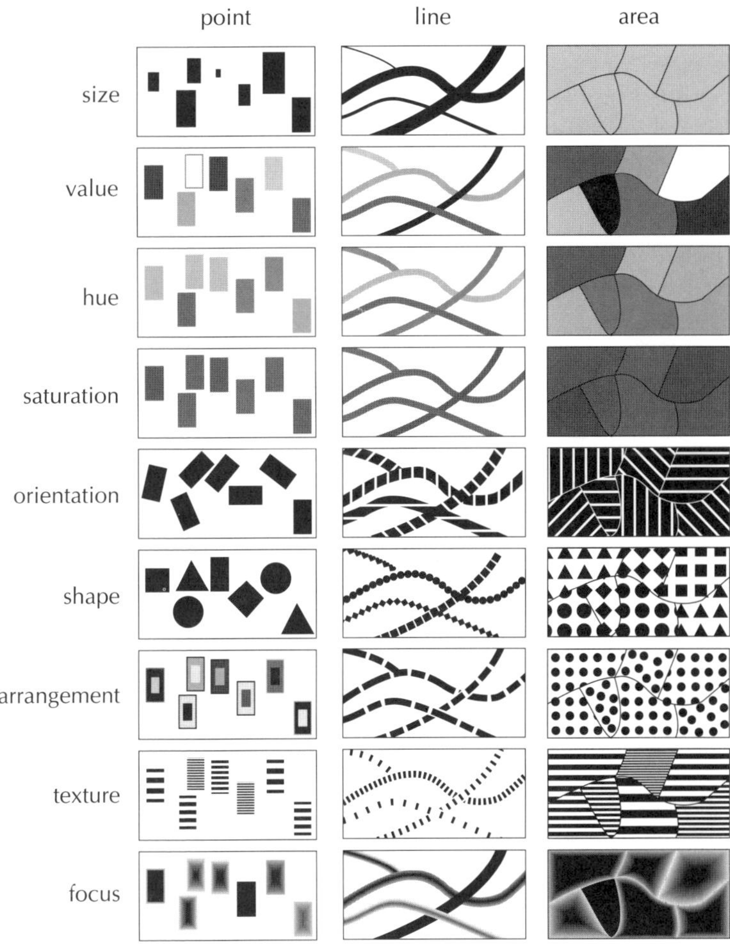


***Figure 2.04*** *Graphic variables available for point, line, area, and volume representation (after DiBiase, et al. 1991) Due to the difficulty of simulating volume on a static two-dimensional page, only the point, line and area application of the graphic primitives are illustrated here. Volumetric applications are primarily useful in the context of stereoscopic computer displays. Location in the plane is inherent in all of the examples and, therefore, has not been depicted separately in this matrix. See color version, Figure C2.04.*

We seldom expect map readers to extract numerical information from a map. The lower level distinction between ordered and non-ordered (nominal) data, therefore, is considered by cartographers to be the most critical. As a result, graphic variables are generally categorized as being suited or unsuited to depiction of nominal and ordinal information. In general, variables suited to ordinal differentiation can be used for numerical differentiation as well. Bertin (1983), however, has argued that application of ordinal graphic variables to higher measurement levels is not always appropriate. In fact, he states that only x-y position in the plane and size are appropriate for depicting quantities. Bertin's concerns and qualifications will be noted as examples are presented below.

### Location in Space

Position in the plane of a 2D map, or above that plane in a 3D map is clearly at the numerical level of measurement (which implies that ordinal information is embedded within it). With a set of dividers or other measuring tools (a ruler or electronic planimeter), numerical information at the discrete or continuous level can be obtained by "measuring" the distance between locations and translating the measurement according to the map scale. In the absence of a measuring device (or the need to be that precise) relative position on an ordinal scale can be visually determined quite effectively (e.g., the distance from Washington, D.C. to Denver is obviously greater than from Washington to Atlanta and the latter distance is clearly shorter than that from Atlanta to Denver) . See Figure 2.05.

If the representational device allows viewing in stereo, we can make use of location in three rather than two-dimensions. With the advent of computer mapping and GIS, many techniques have been devised to facilitate generation of 3D views of data and space. These include anaglyph and other double-image displays that require special glasses that filter the separate images to each eye where our visual system merges them to a stereo view, holographic images that embed several views into one, and computer display hardware that stimulates our visual system to see a 3D image directly (Kraak 1988; Moellering 1989).

*Figure 2.05 A reference map showing the location of Washington, Atlanta and Denver.*

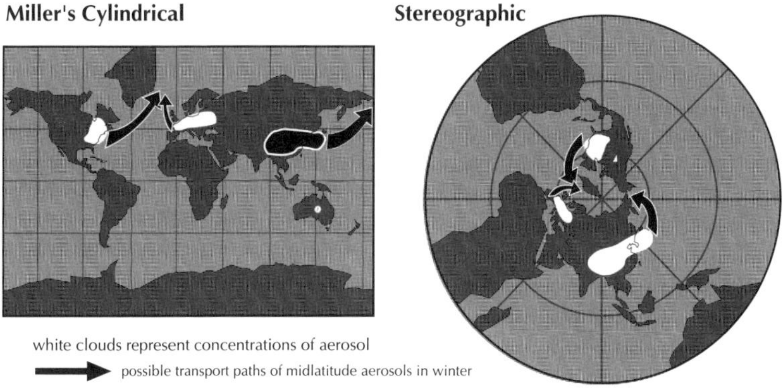

***Figure 2.06*** *This figure illustrates two views of the sources for aerosol pollutants that affect the Arctic. On the left, the Miller's cylindrical projection exaggerates distances among the source locations and makes sources in North America and Asia appear to be unrelated. On the right, a polar stereographic projection is used to place the focus more appropriately on the interconnectedness of sources for arctic aerosol pollutants. Source: Rahn (1982).*

Location in the plane (or in 3D space) is a seemingly direct, unambiguous, graphic variable. On a 2D or 3D scatterplot location is unambiguous. When the representation is of any significant portion of the earth, however, the earth's roughly spherical shape introduces uncertainty into our perception of location.

Maps of hemispherical and global phenomena present the extreme cases. Two locations can appear to be near or far (wherever they are in geographic space) depending upon what projection we use and where we place the interruption(s) (Figure 2.06).[4]

## Size

Changing symbol size is an intuitive representation device for making ordinal distinctions. In Figure 2.07 (page 21), the circles represent pollutant concentrations on an ordinal scale. Even without a legend, few map readers would assume any relationship other than large = high, medium = moderate, and small = low. Size is particularly effective in this kind of application because sizes are easily differentiated by human perception and larger symbols are more visible (stand out more) than smaller symbols.

Size is also well suited to representing numerical information. On the map of hazardous waste shipments by rail provided in Figure 2.08 (page 21), few readers would have trouble estimating that the flow from the southern plant was three times that from the northeastern, which was equal to that from the northwestern. Because size is so easily associated with order and quantities, it should be avoided as a variable when nominal distinctions are to be made. If, for example, a map is created to depict the location of the main concentrations of three endangered species, a completely erroneous conclusion (about the number of individuals left or relative potential for extinction) might be reached if size of symbol was used to distinguish among the three species (Figure 2.09).

### Shape

The appropriate applications of shape are essentially the opposite of that for size. The shape of point symbols or of individual marks making up patterned lines or areas, indicates no inherent order. Shape, therefore, is suited to representation of nominal differences (i.e., differences in kind of thing). In the endangered species example above, substitution of three different shapes for the three circle sizes produces a map much less likely to mislead (Figure 2.10). Unlike size, however, human vision is not particularly sensitive to variation in shapes. If the shapes are small, as is common for point and line symbols on maps, they are sometimes difficult to distinguish at a glance. According to Bertin, therefore, shape (while appropriate for showing nominal distinctions) results in maps that must be "read" (or studied carefully one symbol at a time), rather than "seen" (or understood at a glance). As is clear in Figure 2.11, shapes of the same size tend to look alike if they are small and numerous. The concentration of nuclear reactors in the southeast which is apparent when they are mapped alone is hard to find on the map with varying shape symbols.

### Color Value

Color value is the term applied to variation in darkness or lightness of a color. High values are light (e.g., white or yellow) and low values are dark (e.g., black or navy blue). Unlike size, value has a finite scale from pure white to pure black which in cartography and printing is often specified as a percent black from 0% to 100%. Although this specification is convenient, it can hide the fact that the term "value" is usually applied to the human sensation of brightness which does not correspond in a direct linear way to measured reflectance from a printed page (see Chapter 5).

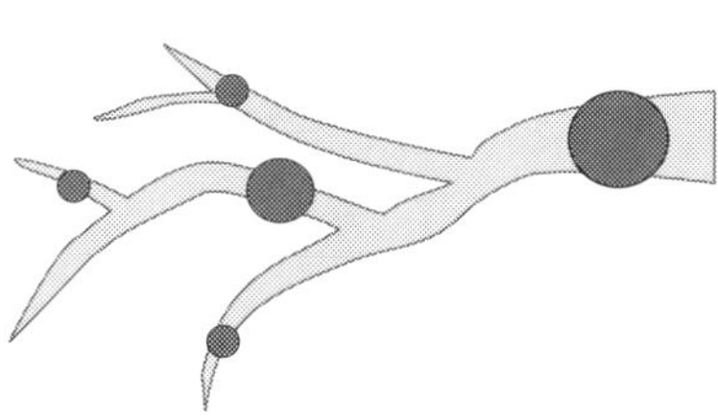

***Figure 2.07*** *Given this map on which circles represent water quality assessments, at which locations have tests indicated water to have "high","moderate," and "low" pollutant levels?*

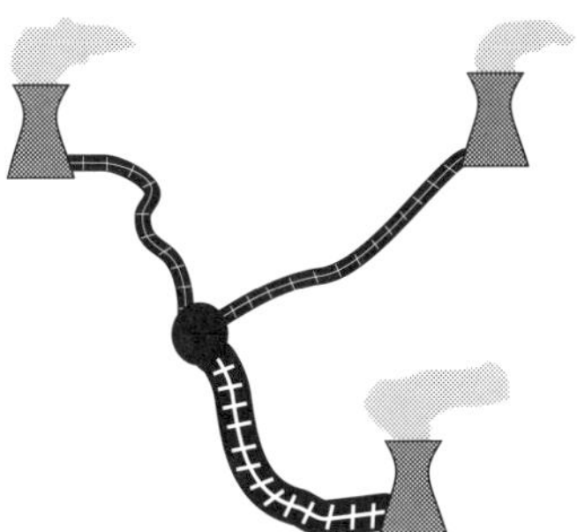

***Figure 2.08*** *This schematic map depicts tons of hazardous waste shipped to a disposal site from three adjacent states.*

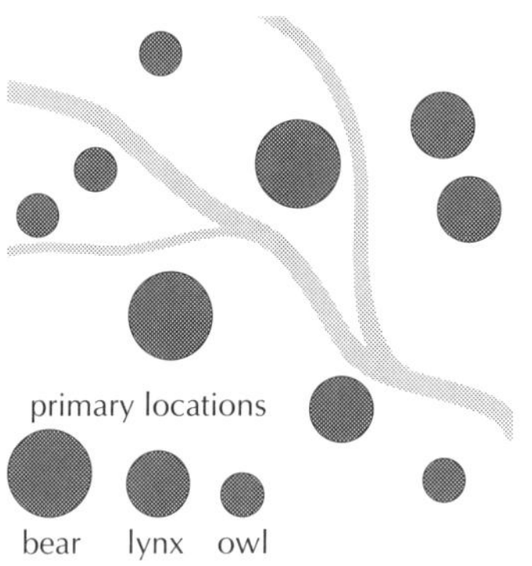


***Figure 2.09*** *This map depicts the primary locations at which bear, lynx, and owl currently exist.*

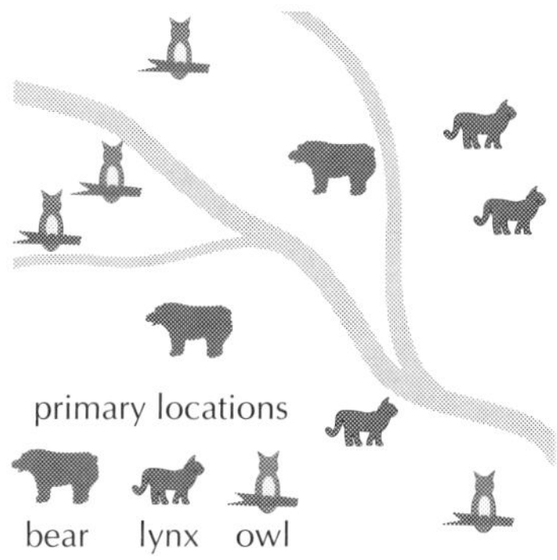


***Figure 2.10*** *The same map as in Figure 2.09 with the abstract symbols replaced by image-related symbols.*

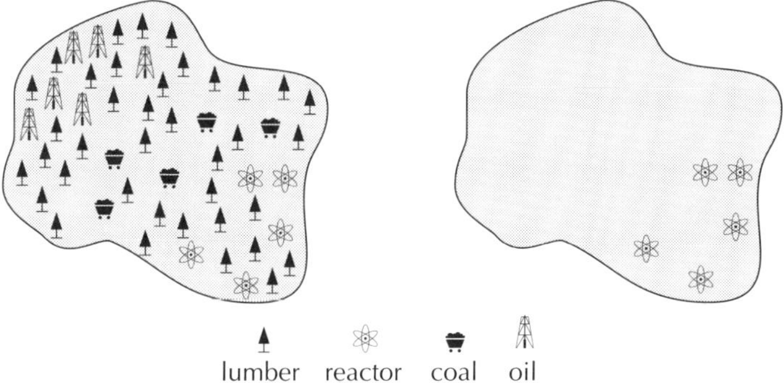


***Figure 2.11*** *Discriminability problems with numerous small shapes makes it hard to visually isolate any single symbol.*

Like size, value clearly has an order. It is, therefore, an appropriate graphic variable for depicting ordinal data. Most cartographers also consider it appropriate to represent magnitudes with a range of values. When value is used to represent magnitudes, however, color value is seldom matched to data values in a proportional way as we do with size. If we apply value differences proportionally, we generally produce uninformative maps as illustrated by the map of ecoregion risk shown in Figure 2.12. This map shows us little because human vision cannot distinguish many shades of gray. With skewed data, as found here, the categories at one end of the scale are similar. Assignment of proportionally similar color value for area fills results in imperceptible differences between units in adjacent categories. Due to this limited human ability to distinguish gray tones, numerical data are usually treated as ordinal when a color value range is applied. Equal visual steps in color value are then used to represent the rank order of categories rather than the numerical differences between them.

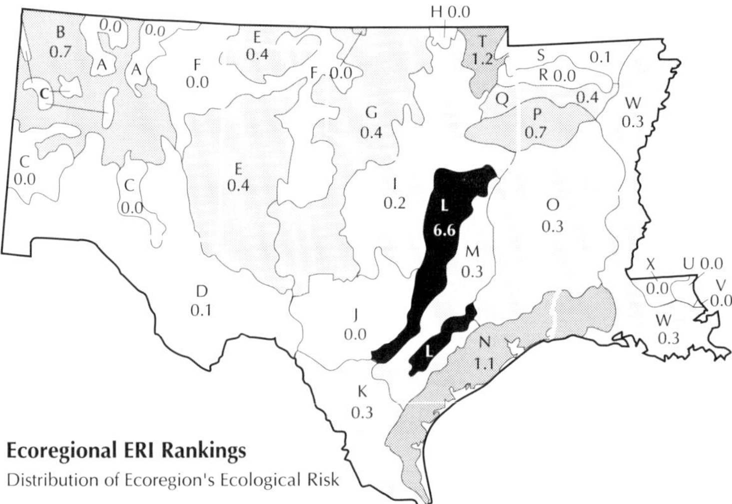


***Figure 2.12** This map represents a range of 0.0 to 6.6 by matching the brightness of area fills to the data values in a direct linear fashion. The low value of 0.0, therefore, is depicted with white, the high value of 6.6 is depicted with black, and remaining values are depicted with a shade of gray corresponding to their position in the range (e.g., the value of 1.2 is 18% of the range greater than the lowest value; therefore, it is depicted as 18% black).*

## Color Hue

When the word "color" is used, most people think of the color attribute known as "hue". Color hue is the term applied to the difference in sensation most people perceive between red, green, blue, etc. Specifically, hue is a measure of the wavelengths that a surface reflects (or emits in the case of a color computer monitor). Different hues are perceived for reflection at different points on the electromagnetic spectrum (Figure 2.13). Visible "colors" (i.e., hues), range from long wavelength reflections (for red and orange) to medium (for yellow and green) to short (for blue and violet).

Humans have relatively high visual acuity for color hue (with the exception of about 8% of the population, almost entirely male, who have some form of color vision deficiency). Hue, therefore, is a particularly good variable for differentiating among different kinds of feature (i.e., making nominal differentiations). Acuity for hue, however, drops off rapidly as the size of area covered by the hue decreases (e.g., for small point symbols) or when peripheral vision must be relied upon to view the map (e.g., when features at unknown locations must be searched for).

With the many hues available at the touch of a button in most GIS environments, together with our relatively good ability to distinguish between hues, it is tempting to use hue differences on all maps. A common mistake made in assigning visual variables to map features in a GIS environment is to apply hue differences to the representation of ordered or numerical data. The problem with applying hue differences to ordered or numerical data is that although there is a logical order to hues (defined by the order of hues in the electromagnetic spectrum), many people do not know

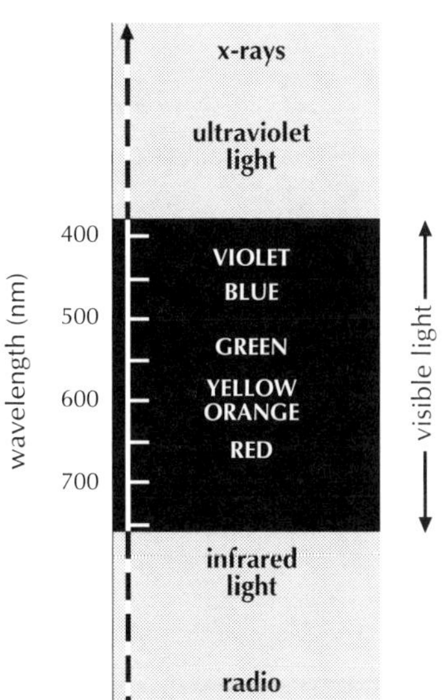


*Figure 2.13* *The electromagnetic spectrum with commonly named colors and their wavelengths.*

the order and even for those who do, value differences among hues overwhelm our perception. Consider, for example the data depicted on map A in Figure 2.14. If a value range of six categories from white to black is used to represent the data, an obvious northeast-southwest pattern emerges from the map without any real need to know what is being mapped or what specific values each gray tone represents. If, on the other hand, a spectrally ordered hue range is applied, the northeast-southwest pattern disappears and is replaced by a false impression of a southeast-northwest pattern. As Bertin (1981) has pointed out, using a range of hues ordered by value rather than by spectral order can eliminate this visual distortion. A set of hues arrayed by value stimulates the correct perception and also has the advantage of generating more interest and creating somewhat greater visual contrast between categories than is apparent on the black and white map.

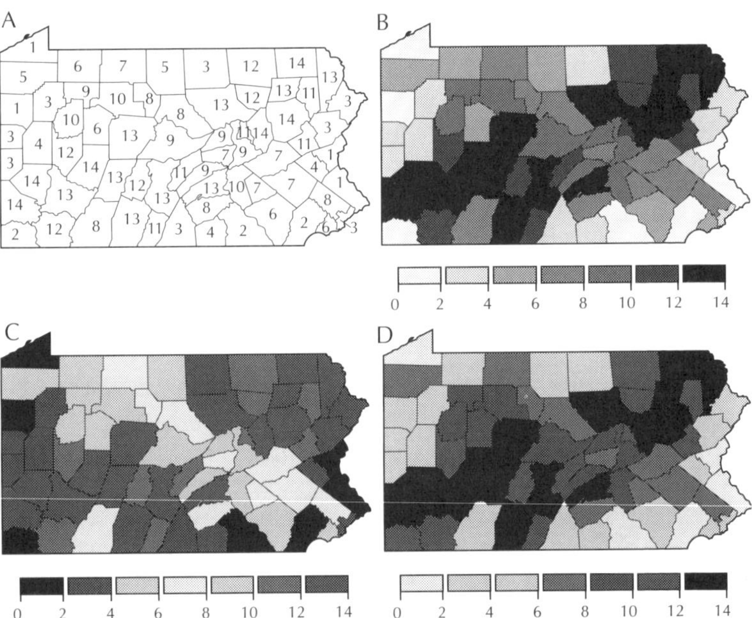


***Figure 2.14*** *This sequence of maps shows the difference in visual impression of pattern that is produced if the data in map A are depicted using a value range (map B), a spectrally ordered hue range (map C), or a hue range ordered by value (map D). This illustration was inspired by a similar series in Bertin (1981, p. 220). See color version, Figure C2.14.*

If we think about this combined use of hue and value and consider the electromagnetic spectrum shown in Figure 2.13 again, it becomes apparent that the colors of the spectrum array themselves quite nicely into two value ranges. The highest value hue of the spectrum (yellow) occupies the center of the spectrum. Hues decrease in value in both directions from yellow. This results in two hue-value sequences that are appropriate for representation of ordinal information on maps: A) yellow through green to blue or violet, and B) yellow through orange to red. If we apply both of these ranges to the maps of Figure 2.14, we see that the northeast-southwest distribution is revealed and that the yellow to red sequence does a somewhat better job of highlighting it (Figure 2.15).

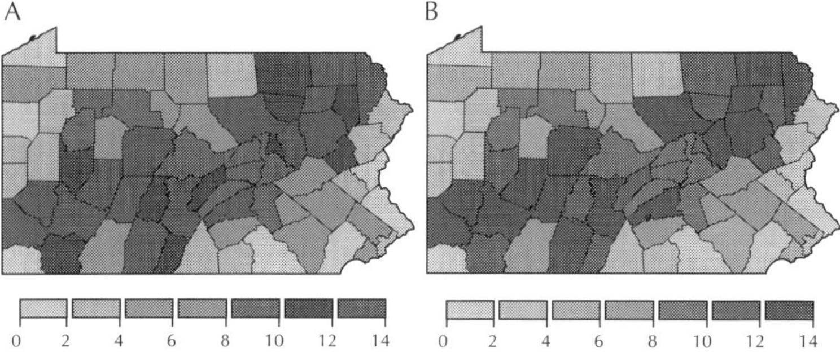


***Figure 2.15*** *The distribution mapped in Figure 2.14 is depicted here with a part-spectral sequence of hues from yellow to violet and from yellow to red. See color version, Figure C2.15.*

## Color Saturation

Color saturation, like color value, presents an obvious visual order. While color value is an available variable for both black and white and color maps, color saturation is defined only in the color context. Saturation can be thought of as the purity of a hue. More precisely, it is the range of wavelengths reflected (or emitted) from a particular map location. If a narrow range of wavelengths is reflected a pure, very recognizable hue results. If, on the other hand, reflectance includes wavelengths from a wide portion of the spectrum, the perception is of a mixture of hues with no one hue dominant—an impure or muddy color (Figure 2.16, page 26). At the extreme, if all wavelengths are reflected the perception is of white or gray, no hue (or all hues) dominant.

Applying saturation differences to our example map reveals the northeast-southwest distribution (Figure 2.17). Saturation, however, is seldom used as a graphic variable in isolation. Together with value or hue differences, changes in saturation can enhance the perception of order and/or extend the perceptible range of categories that can be included on the map. Combining saturation with a part-spectral hue range, for example, makes the distribution of our sample map more apparent (Figure 2.18).

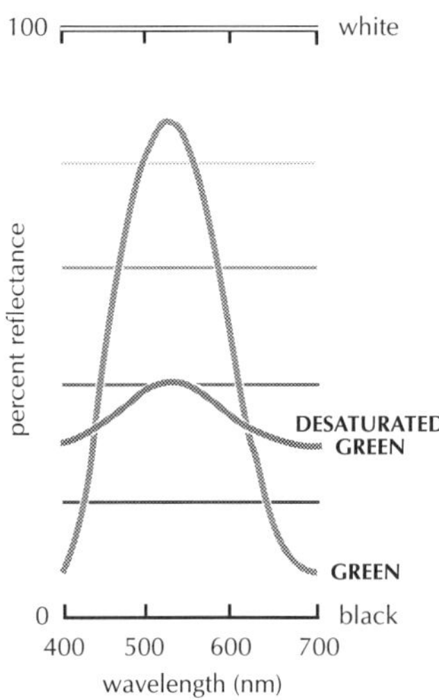


*Figure 2.16* This plot of reflected wavelengths illustrates a relatively pure green and the same green at lower saturation (with a greater mix of reflected wavelengths).

*Figure 2.17* The sample map from Figure 2.14 with categories represented by a range in saturation, which in black and white become indiscriminable. See color version, Figure C2.17.

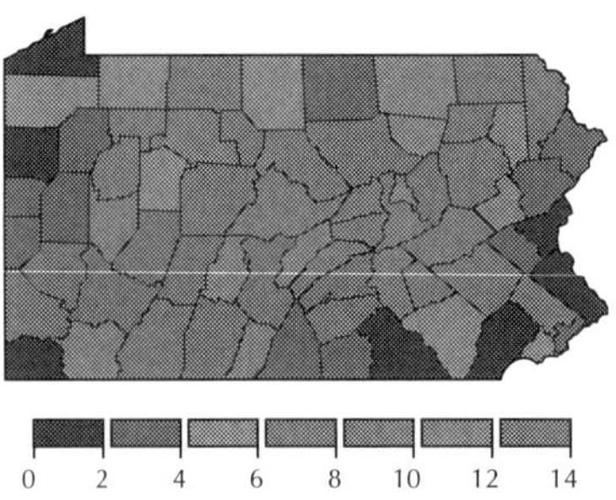


*Figure 2.18* The example map with saturation differences combined with a part-spectral hue range that better reveals the east–west distribution. See color version, Figure C2.18.

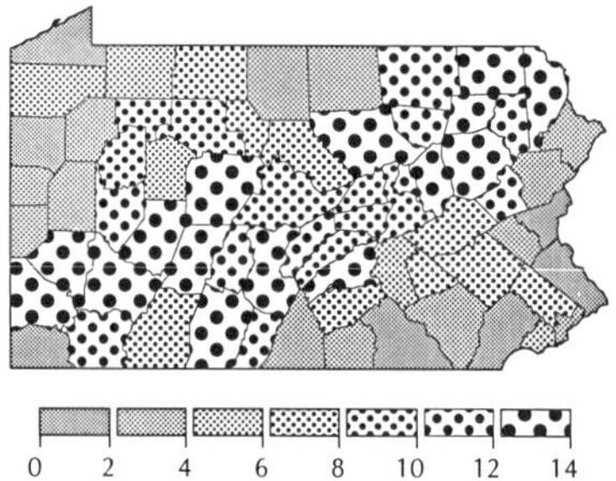


*Figure 2.19* The example map with texture differences used to indicate low to high value categories.

### Texture

Texture refers to the spatial frequency of components of a pattern. Because it is only defined for patterns, relatively large areas are required for texture differences to be obvious. It is, therefore, most suited to differentiation among areas, although two or maybe three categories can be created by changing the texture of elements that make up point or line symbols.

There is an obvious order to texture, from fine to coarse, and texture could be applied to the representation of ordinal categories for areas (Figure 2.19). Although the northeast-southwest pattern is apparent, other symbolization methods are clearly superior to a texture range for a seven category choropleth map.

The other attribute of texture that is more important for its use as a graphic variable is the human ability to notice texture differences at a glance. Some psychologists, for example, feel that texture gradient (the fact that any regular texture will appear finer with distance) is an important cue for depth perception. Coarse textures stand out because they appear to be closer to us than fine textures. As a result, texture is ideally suited to creating visual separation between layers of information. Figure 2.20 (page 28), for example, illustrates a case in which the Deasy GeoGraphics Lab at Penn State combined texture, value, and size to visually sort out seven categories of information that were barely perceptible on the client's original sketch map (Figure 2.21, page 28).

Texture is also useful as a way to visually separate the two ends of a double-ended distribution, such as on a map of respiratory cancer in which it is important to isolate those counties with incidence above and below the national average (Figure 2.22, page 29).

### Arrangement

Arrangement, like texture, is an element of pattern. It is, therefore, most appropriate for area symbols, although it has limited application to point and line symbols. Arrangement depends on the relative position of symbol elements and, when applied to an area, can range from regular to random. Although this implies an order, it is not a very obvious order and is probably not effective in representing ordinal data (Figure 2.23, page 30). There are prob-

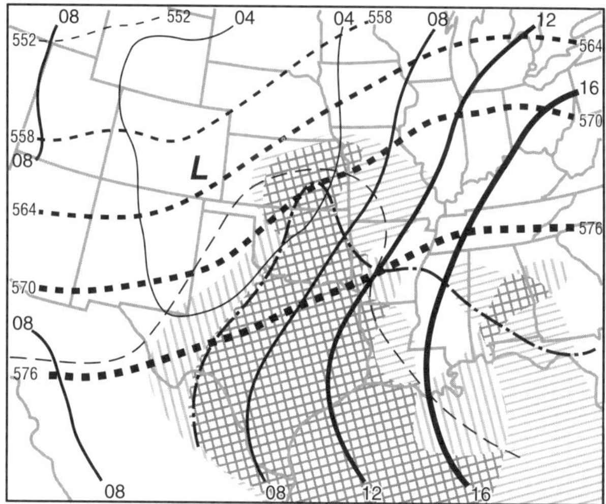


*Figure 2.20* This map illustrates the use of texture and value differences to sort out seven layers of overlapping information: mean sea-level isobars (thick solid contours), mean 500 mb heights (thick dashed contours), a mean surface 55°F dewpoint isopleth (thin dot-dashed contour), a mean 700 mb 6°C isotherm (thin dashed contour), areas of greater than 50% frequency of unstable buoyancy (shading with thin, nearly vertical hatches), the presence of a capping inversion with a well-mixed layer above (shading with thick, nearly horizontal hatches), and the region of overlap, where the capping inversion overlies buoyantly unstable air (shading with thick cross hatches).

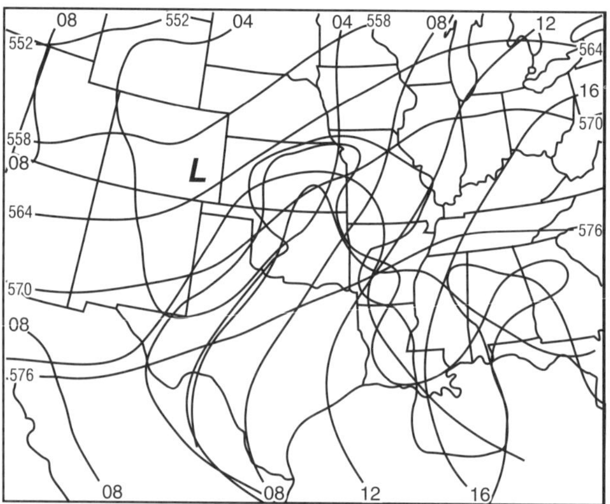


*Figure 2.21* The same data shown in Figure 2.20, plotted without the benefit of any graphic design strategies.

**INCIDENCE OF CANCER OF THE TRACHEA, BRONCHUS, LUNG AND PLEURA, 1986**

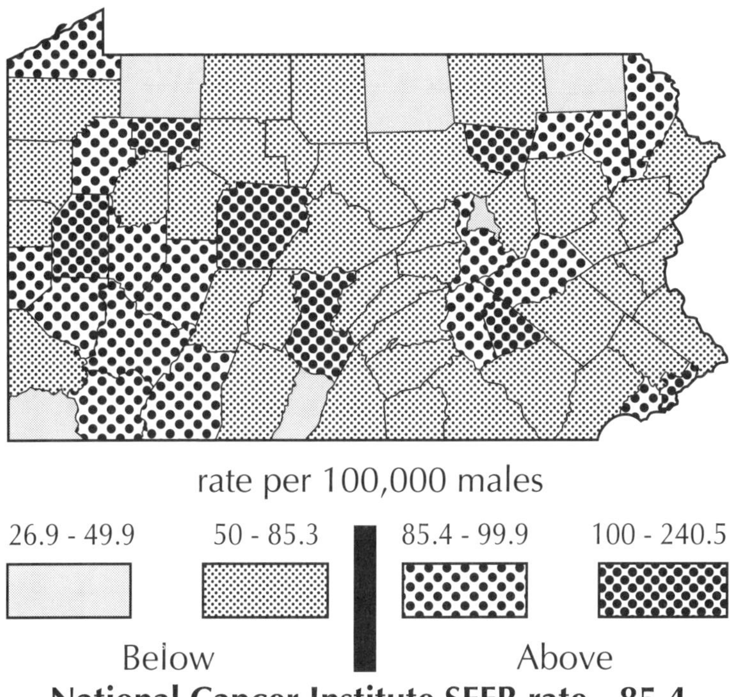


***Figure 2.22*** *In this map, the cancer rate per 100,000 males by county in Pennsylvania is represented. Counties in which the rate is above the national average are indicated by the coarse area patterns and those below the national average are indicated by the fine patterns. Source: Cancer Incidence and Mortality in Pennsylvania, 1986. Pennsylvania Department of Health (1990).*

ably only three noticeable steps along the random to regular arrangement continuum.

More important than the implied order that different arrangements might communicate, is the range of distinctive symbols that can result from various arrangements of symbol elements. With line symbols, for example, a variety of different categories can be represented without suggesting that one is more important than the other (Figure 2.24, page 30). With area patterns, changing the arrangement of pattern elements in a set of gray tones can enhance the discriminability of the value steps (Figure 2.25, page 30).

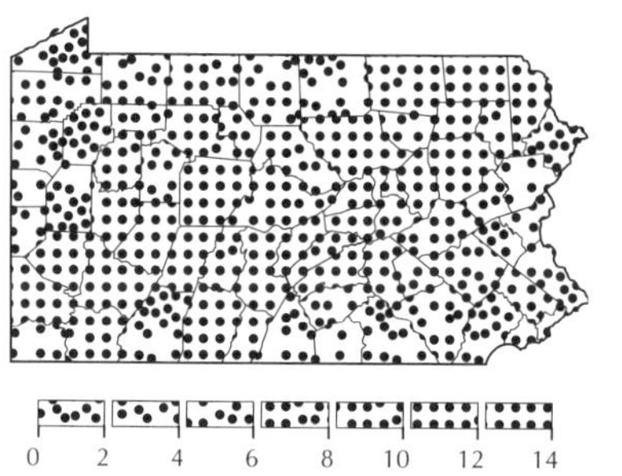


*Figure 2.23* The example map with the data depicted by a set of area fills that range from random distribution of dots to a regular grid pattern.

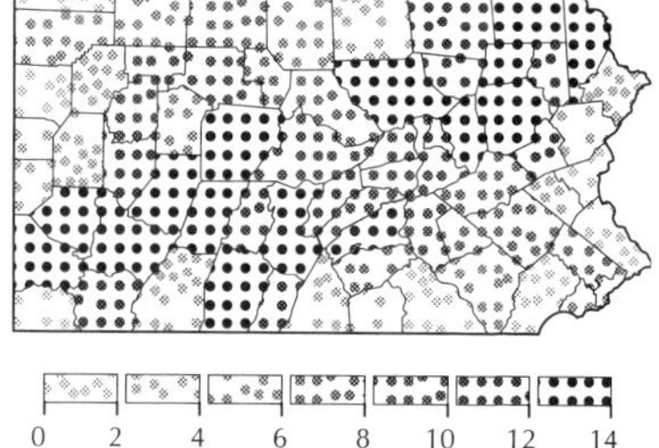


*Figure 2.25* The example map with a range of random to regular dots patterns combined with a value range.

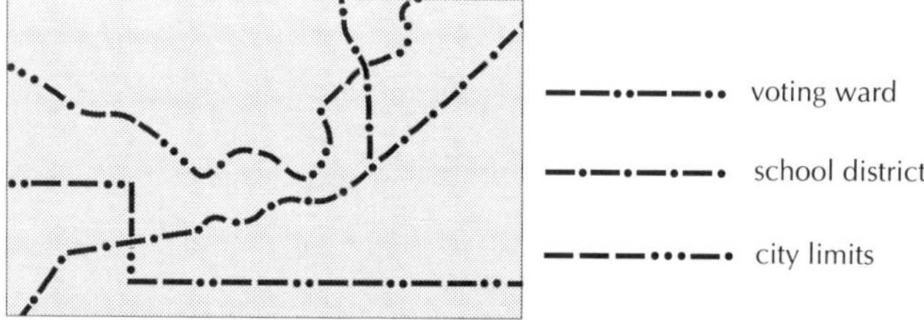


*Figure 2.24* A set of three overlapping boundaries in which different arrangements of dots and dashes are used to create a non-ordered set of distinctions.

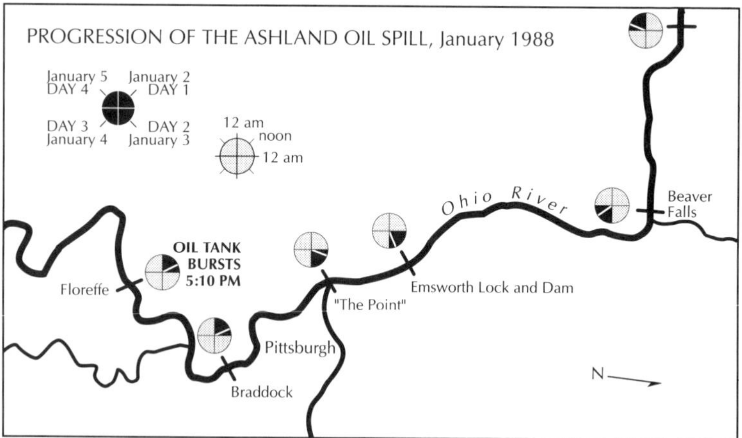


*Figure 2.26* A map showing progress of the Ashland Oil Spill near Pittsburgh, PA in 1988. Orientation of the hands on a "clock" clearly indicates order—of time. Source: Pennsylvania Emergency Management Agency. After Action Report, Ashland Oil Spill, January 2, 1988 (1990).

*Figure 2.27 The same data as shown in Figure 2.11 are depicted. Differences in symbol shape are replaced by differences in orientation, making individual categories easy to differentiate.*

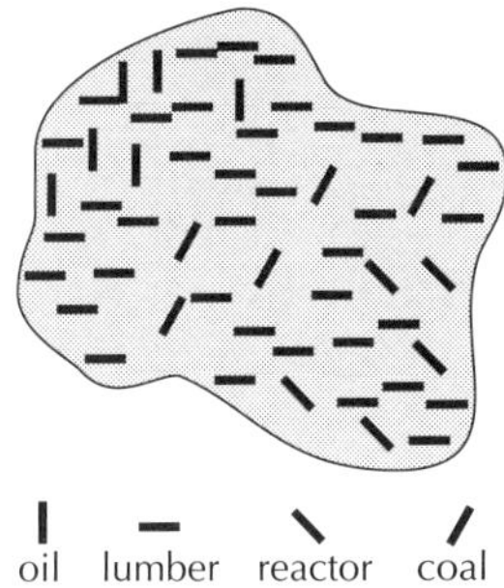


## Orientation

Orientation is a graphic variable that is too often used arbitrarily and, therefore, ineffectively. As Bertin (1983) has illustrated, orientation differences are very noticeable and we can take good advantage of them in differentiating among nominal variables. Cells of the brain have been found to be selectively sensitive to different orientations (Hubel 1988). Orientation can be an effective variable, therefore, because human vision is "hard-wired" to be sensitive to it. The "noticeability" of orientation differences might be particularly important in exploratory applications where patterns are being sought with few preconceptions about their potential form and location.

Like texture and arrangement, orientation can imply order in limited ways (e.g., by use of modified clock face symbols on a map showing when a toxic spill passed particular points in a river)(Figure 2.26). Again, however, it is the ability of orientation to differentiate without implying order or emphasizing one category over another that is its particularly appealing aspect as a graphic variable. A comparison of the use of shape and orientation of point symbols in differentiating among four categories of densely distributed point features makes the advantages of orientation over shape quite clear (Figure 2.27). For nominal features, orientation is also superior to size because no one category is emphasized over another.

## Focus

Focus refers to the clarity of a symbol or the extent to which details are visible.[5] Similar to color saturation, focus can change from unambiguous (i.e., a sharp image with no doubt about what you are looking at) to ambiguous (i.e., a fuzzy or imprecise representation).

Due to this link with certainty or doubt, focus seems to be ideally suited to depiction of certainty or uncertainty about a location or attributes at that location.

Defocusing can be created by fading from one color at the center of a symbol to the background color at the edges (see Figure 2.03). In addition, it might be possible to simulate a fog or haze between the viewer and a symbol or to decrease spatial resolution.

Focus is a graphic variable that has received almost no attention in the literature. At this point it remains uncertain how useful a variable it will prove to be. In chapter four, we will consider some of its possible applications to depiction of uncertainty.

## Summary

This chapter has addressed the basic units of cartographic (i.e., "map") language and how to apply these units to representing features of the environment. A good starting point for any mapping problem is to categorize the features to be mapped according to their dimensionality and their level of measurement. It is best to match the dimensionality of symbols to the dimensionality with which you choose to represent the environment (e.g., features that are interpreted as positional at a particular scale and for a particular purpose should be represented with point symbols). In addition, the map maker should select from the available graphic variables to match the level of measurement at which data are to be represented.[6] The graphic variables also have considerable variation in their ability to visually differentiate among features or categories of features, to visually isolate features, and to draw selected features to the foreground of the map to produce visual levels. The chart on the facing page, therefore, has been designed as an aid in determining the applicability of each graphic variable described above to particular representational problems (Figure 2.28).

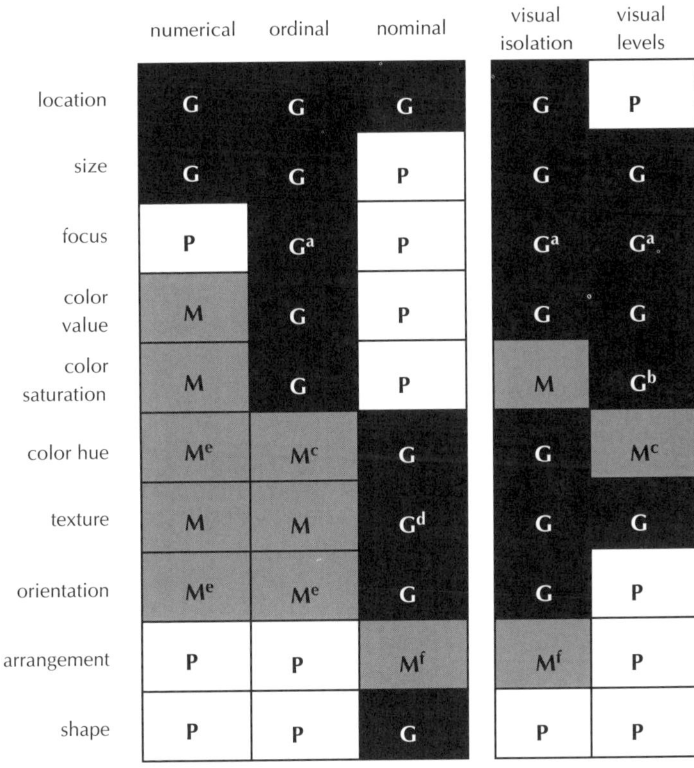

| | numerical | ordinal | nominal | visual isolation | visual levels |
|---|---|---|---|---|---|
| location | G | G | G | G | P |
| size | G | G | P | G | G |
| focus | P | G[a] | P | G[a] | G[a] |
| color value | M | G | P | G | G |
| color saturation | M | G | P | M | G[b] |
| color hue | M[e] | M[c] | G | G | M[c] |
| texture | M | M | G[d] | G | G |
| orientation | M[e] | M[e] | G | G | P |
| arrangement | P | P | M[f] | M[f] | P |
| shape | P | P | G | P | P |

**G = good, M = marginally effective, P = poor**

*Figure 2.28* *Representational uses to which graphic variables are suited. This chart summarizes the applications for which the graphic variables discussed above are appropriate. These guidelines are elaborated upon in notes keyed to blocks of the chart:*

*[a]Focus can be used for no more than two or three categories. The drawback of this variable is that defocused symbols may be interpreted as error and/or may be hard to look at. This variable is untested and may prove to be most effective in an interactive environment where it can be turned on or off when an indication of data quality is desired.*

*[b]Purer, more saturated colors appear to be in the foreground, while dull, desaturated colors fade into the background.*

*[c]Hues must be carefully selected for an order or hierarchy to be apparent (e.g., the part-spectral sequence from yellow through orange to red). Hues interact with one another in sometimes unpredictable ways, so it is often difficult to determine which hues will appear dominant over others.*

*[d]Pattern texture is good for only two or perhaps three identifiable categories.*

*[e]Orientation provides limited ability to communicate numerical or ordered information through use of standardized signs such as a clock face symbol to communicate time of occurrence, a meteorological wind direction flag to indicate direction, or a geologic strike and dip symbol to indicate amount and direction of slope for outcrop layers.*

*[f]Pattern arrangement is best as a redundant variable to make a visual difference between categories more obvious.*

## Endnotes

[1]*For a more formalized account of mapping as a language, see Head (1984). The approach presented in this chapter uses 'language' in the broader sense of a semiotic system, or system of signs. See Schlichtmann (1985) and Wood (1992) for other views on map semiotics.*

[2]*The original version of this typology appeared in French, in 1967.*

[3]*For extensions to three-dimensional symbols, tactile symbols, dynamic symbols, and audio symbols see Kraak (1988), Vasconcellos (1993), DiBiase, et al. (1992), and Krygier (in press), respectively.*

[4]*For a good overview of how to make effective use of map projections see ACSM (1988 and 1991).*

[5]*Focus was initially suggested as a graphic variable in a seminar by Woodward at the University of Wisconsin (DiBiase 1991, personal communication).*

[6]*See Morrison (1984) for a detailed case study in which this approach is applied to symbolization choice for atlas maps.*

# 3

# Abstracting Reality

*Maps and map symbols are all abstractions, but the degree of abstraction can vary tremendously. Map designers must know how much abstraction is appropriate to a particular application or user and what kind of abstraction to apply. One of the most important abstraction decisions for the map designer is how to classify (or categorize) the phenomena being represented. In addition, the map designer will always be faced with a choice about the cartographic language to use (i.e., choices among symbols for representing the specific categories delineated). This latter choice should, where possible, rely on "logical" connections between the symbol variables and the topic depicted. Issues of data classification and symbol logic are both particularly important with numerical data depiction where there are often no predetermined category or symbol systems of the kind developed for some categorical information (e.g., geologic structures).*

## The Image to Graphic Continuum

GIS puts a variety of display tools at our disposal for representing spatial information. These tools vary in degree of abstraction from *images* that mimic what an observer sees from a particular vantage point (e.g., a photograph of waste drums in a swamp or a remotely sensed image used in landscape characterization) to *graphics* that represent relationships that may or may not be visible and may not even have a spatial extent (e.g., stream velocity over time or potential for ground water contamination with distance from a waste disposal site) (Figure 3.01, page 38).

The fundamental distinction between images and graphics is that images are composed of marks that have no independently defined meaning (i.e., lines, tones, shades), whereas graphics consist of relatively unambiguous *symbols* precisely defined by convention or a key. The result is a difference in emphasis from questions of "what is that?" on the part of the viewer to "what are the relations, in an abstract sense, among the things symbolized?" (MacEachren

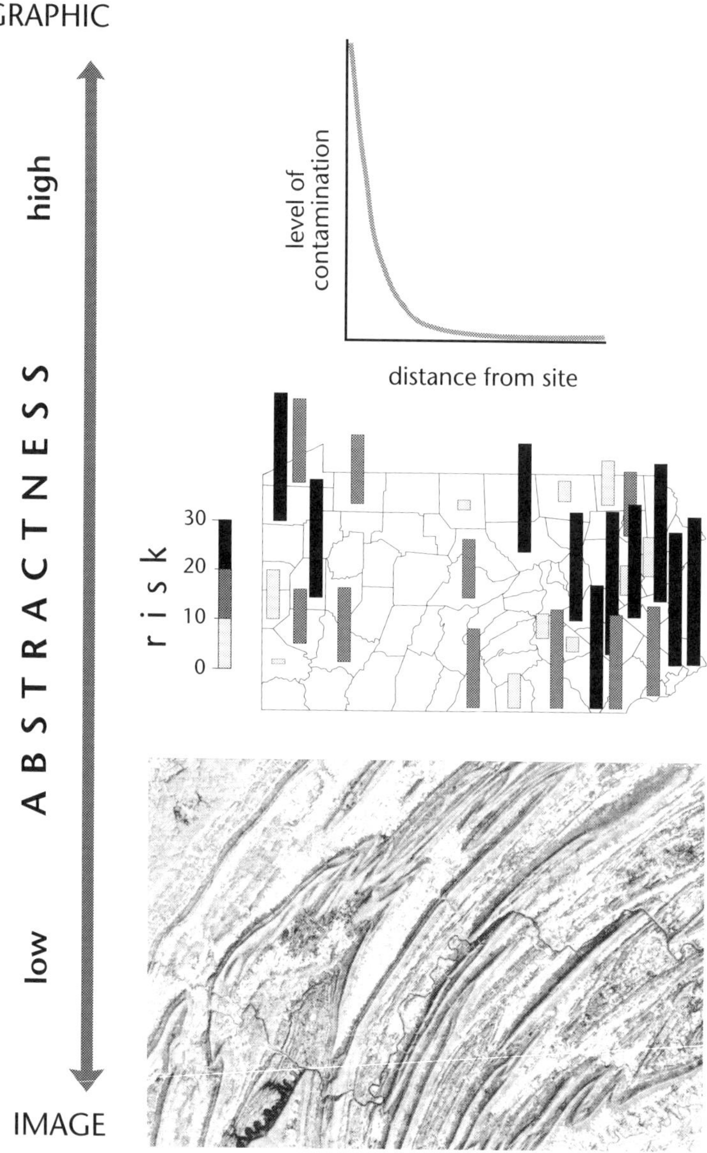


*Figure 3.01 Image-graphic continuum. Top - A distance decay diagram showing the expected decrease in ground water contamination potential with distance from a waste disposal site. Middle - The map depicts categories of ground water risk for the 30 Pennsylvania counties determined to be at the greatest risk, together with an indication of the specific ranking of each of these counties in the risk assessment. Source EPA 1990a. Bottom - portion of a Landsat image of central Pennsylvania.*

and Ganter 1990). With images, representation choices are a function of information collection procedures with the analyst simply left with the task of interpreting what is seen. As we move toward the graphic end of the continuum, however, there is an increasing number of abstraction decisions left to the analyst/map designer.

For environmental analysis, remote sensing exemplifies the image end of the image-graphic continuum (Figure 3.01, bottom). Because remotely sensed representations are generally closer than maps to the reality they represent (i.e., they have been subjected to less abstraction), they present a rich opportunity for exploratory data analysis but require considerable skill and knowledge on the analyst's part to recognize patterns and relationships.

Not all remotely sensed "images" are images according to the above definition. While an aerial photograph provides a depiction similar to direct visual perception, a thermal IR scene or other non-photographic "image" matches colors or tones to an electromagnetic signal that might be derived from a non-visible source (i.e., temperature). The thermal IR and similar remotely sensed scenes are, therefore, more abstract than an aerial photograph. The analyst/map designer using GIS to relate thermal IR scenes to other spatial information begins to be faced with abstraction decisions not required of the air photo interpreter (e.g., how many color steps the signal should be mapped onto).

When we reach the midpoint of the image-graphic continuum, viewers must learn the linkage between referents (the things represented) and the signs (e.g., map symbols) used to represent them. A land use map derived from a Landsat scene or a small scale map of risk to ground water provide clear examples (Figure 3.01, center). In the case of the ground water risk map, once the linkage between referent (categories of increasing risk to ground water) and sign (filled graduated bars) is understood (bar height and value provide redundant indications of risk with larger, darker bars indicating greater risk), rapid and accurate recognition of patterns and relationships becomes possible. In this case, it is clear that the region surrounding Philadelphia dominates the ground water vulnerability problems of Pennsylvania. In spite of the apparent clarity of presentation maps such as this, the act of symbolizing introduces a conscious recasting of information that can both aid and hinder interpretation by focusing the representation on selected features (e.g., rank ordered composite risk categories versus percent of the population at risk due to unsafe water sources).

Like remotely sensed representations, maps are not restricted to one position on the abstractness continuum. An orthophoto quad (based on rectified aerial photographs), for example, is much less abstract (and less open to interpretation or misinterpretation) than the graduated symbol map of ground water risk or a choropleth map of cancer rate per county.

At the graphic end of the abstractness continuum, we rely on viewers' spatial visualization abilities when we use our graphic variable *location in space* to present ordered or numerical relationships. Location in space is inherently ordered. This allows us to map virtually any variables onto the spatial dimensions and have positions in the resulting graphic space represent position in attribute space. A typical graphic used to supplement map-based analysis is a distance decay diagram that relates interaction to distance (possibly along a selected transect from a potential pollution source) (Figure 3.01, top). In this case, one of the dimensions of 2D space is used for a spatial variable, while the other is used to represent an attribute associated with that space.

## Classification

For any illustrations except those at the extreme image end of the continuum described, information usually must be classified before it can be represented. Symbols on maps, for example, are seldom matched to individual referents, but to classes or categories. On a vegetation map, we would never use different symbols for each individual tree.

In addition to determining the abstractness of the display form, then, a map designer must determine the appropriate level of abstraction for the data to be represented. This decision involves choices about the resolution of the category system by which the environment is described and about the bounds of individual categories. At the exploratory end of our map use continuum, the goal should be to provide analysts with flexibility to alter category resolution and definitions in the search for pattern. As we approach the presentation end of the continuum, particularly when maps are generated for presentation at public meetings, a single category resolution and set of definitions must generally be selected. At this stage we have dual (often competing) goals of making a particular point (and searching for the map that does this well) and presenting data as accurately as possible (however accuracy might be defined).

## Categorical Information

With categorical information, category definition is a subjective process for which we have no well defined rules. After making an initial decision about the general attribute resolution required, a taxonomy of sorts must be devised. One overriding guideline to follow is that ***features that end up in the same category should be more similar to one another than features in different categories.*** The complementary guideline is that ***features that end up in different categories*** *(and as a result are symbolized differently)* ***should be different enough to warrant the distinction.***

The importance of careful attention to category definition (either your own or that of a source) is well illustrated by considering the nominal category of woodlands on USGS topographic sheets and on the Kansas land use-land cover map produced by the University of Kansas Space Technology Laboratories in 1974. Woodland seems like an obvious and unambiguous category to include in a land cover classification. Our initial expectation is that the term "woodland" should mean the same thing, regardless of who generated the map. Intuitively, we might consider the term to apply only to places in which at least half of the area is tree covered. With the Kansas map, woodland is defined somewhat more conservatively, as all areas with 70% or greater tree cover. This contrasts sharply with the USGS definition. Rather surprisingly to many unsuspecting users, the woodland category on USGS topographic maps is defined as an area of 20% or greater tree cover. Unlike the definition used for the Kansas map which was derived as part of a comprehensive land cover classification, the USGS category definition is derived from historical military considerations. When the definition was developed, woodland was defined as any area in which tree cover was "dense enough to conceal troops." This was determined to be 20% and this value is still used to define woodland. Those solid green areas on topo sheets, therefore, may be as little as 20% trees.

## Numerical Information

For numerical information, although it is possible to represent each data value directly using variations in size, color value, or color saturation, it is more common to group data into classes. The classes are usually numerically continguous ranges of values that together cover the entire range of the data set being depicted. The object of classing or grouping values is to remove some of the local detail in the hopes of providing a more easily understood representation of the overall distribution. As with categorical data, how we define the classes is again important. When a single symbol (e.g., circle size, line width, gray shade, etc.) is used to represent all values within the range, all values within the range should be similar.

The number of classes is also critical in determining the impression communicated. The more accuracy desired, the more classes we want. A concern for accuracy will put a lower limit on the number of classes. A one class map is, for example, of no use even though the average value it depicts might be meaningful in certain contexts (Figure 3.02).

An upper limit in terms of number of classes will be determined by a combination of map objectives (e.g., exploration versus confirmation versus synthesis versus presentation) and graphic or perceptual limits. For exploratory representations, an analyst will want a relatively unfiltered (i.e., accurate) view of the environment. If you are not sure what to look for or have a hypothesis that you are not yet very confident in, you will want an opportunity to consider all available information and to sift that information through a variety of filters in an effort to notice and isolate key patterns and relationships. At the extreme, we can have one class for each data value, resulting in a different symbol assigned to each value (Figure 3.03).[1]

As we move from exploration (relatively private visual thinking) toward presentation (more public visual communication), there is a need to begin filtering out local noise so that significant trends in the information become clear. The goal switches from noticing the unexpected to conveying the essense of an analysis or communicating a particular perspective on a problem. A more abstract representation (with fewer categories) is, therefore, generally warranted (Figure 3.04). Although accuracy of depiction decreases as we decrease the number of classes, reducing the number can act to enhance patterns that might otherwise be lost in the detail (Figure 3.05).

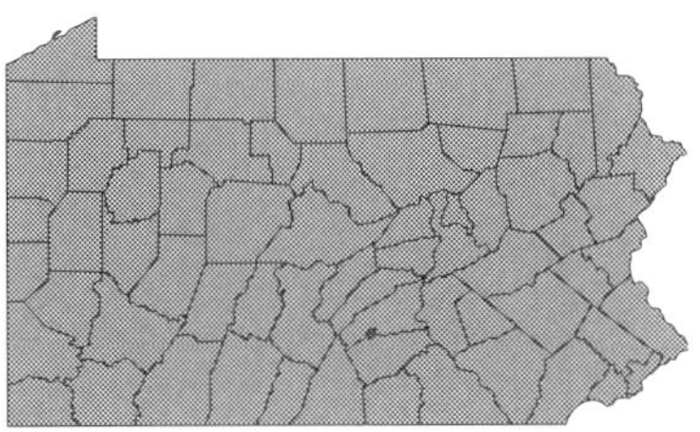

***Figure 3.02*** *A 1-class map of cancer of the trachea, bronchus, lung and pleura (see Fig 2.22).*

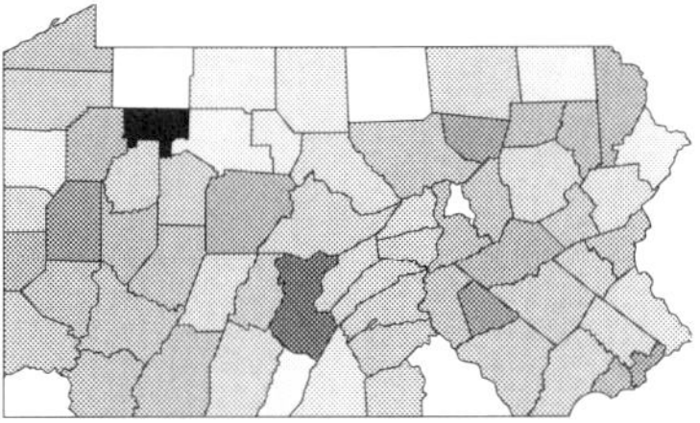

***Figure 3.03*** *An N-class map of cancer of the trachea, bronchus, lung and pleura.*

***Figure 3.04*** *A 5-class map of cancer of the trachea, bronchus, lung and pleura.*

| 7 | 2 | 5 |
|---|---|---|
| 6 | 3 | 4 |
| 7 | 1 | 5 |
| 6 | 2 | 4 |
| 6 | 3 | 4 |

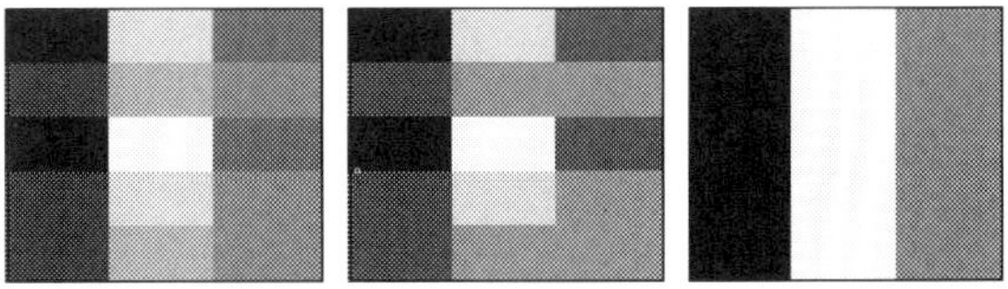

***Figure 3.05*** *A schematic illustration of the potential for abstraction via categorization to enhance a pattern. The right-hand map uses three categories with ranges of 1-3, 4-5, and 6-7. Local detail visible on the five class map (middle) and the seven class map (left) obscures the pattern.*

Particularly when the goal of representation is visual communication, we also need to consider graphic and perceptual limitations. Map readers can distinguish many sizes, shapes, orientations, and color hues, but only a limited number of color value, color saturation, texture, arrangement, and focus differences. For example, outside of a map context people can, on average, distinguish 7 shades of gray from white to black. Embedded in the complexity of a typical map, we can expect no more than 6 color values to be distinguished easily, with even fewer color saturations, textures, or levels of focus.

When we decide to classify numerical data, we encounter many techniques for determining class bounds. Each will impart a unique visual character to a mapped distribution. Selection of class intervals is a function of the map designer's purpose and the characteristics of the data themselves. In some cases, the objective of a map may dictate at least part of the classification system to be used. For example, an air pollution map might use the public air quality advisory level as one class break point and the air quality warning level as another, or a cancer map might use the national mean rate (as done in Figure 2.22). A map showing change in populations of endangered species would probably use zero change as one break point, producing a map that distinguishes between improved and degraded areas. When mapping an ecological risk index, on the other hand it may be appropriate to leave values of zero in a category by themselves (as done on the ecological risk maps prepared for the Region 6 Comparative Risk Project Ecological Report (EPA 1990b)).

Even when one or two logical break points are predetermined, others must be derived using alternative criteria. Let us assume for the moment that there are no predetermined break points for classifying or grouping a particular set of data. As an example we will examine the EPA Region 6 ecological risk index values for physical degradation of terrestrial ecosystems/habitat due to urban sources found in the Region 6 Comparative Risk Project Ecological Report (EPA 1990b)(Figure 3.06). Consider how we might divide these data into a small number of classes for use on a choropleth map (i.e., a map in which area fills are applied to unit areas to depict numerical categories to which those areas are assigned).[2]

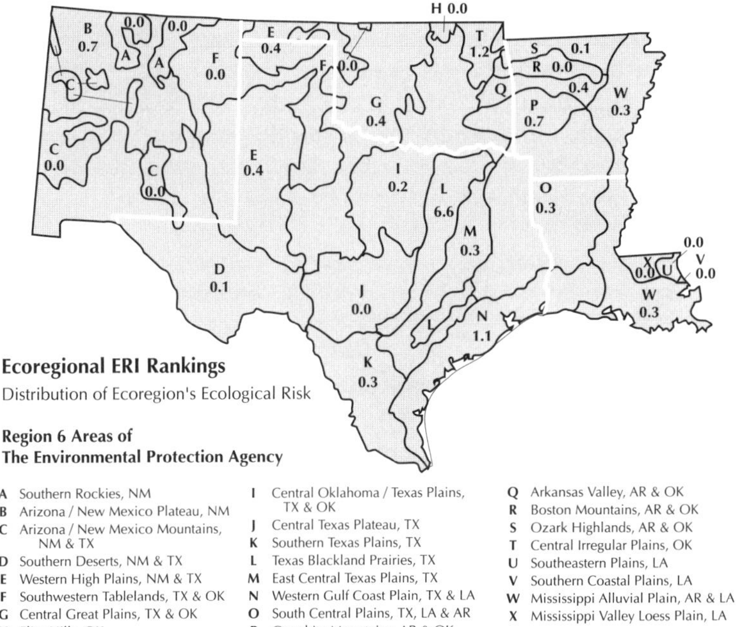


***Figure 3.06*** *Risk index totals by ecological region.*

Many GIS and computer mapping packages provide two default choices for classifying numerical data along with an option for the user to enter externally determined class break points.[3] Our risk index data will illustrate why ***default data classification procedures should be avoided!***

One criterion for selecting data classes often cited in textbooks is that the class breaks assigned should result in roughly equal numbers of data values in each category. This criteria is intuitively appealing. If you plan to have five classes symbolized by five shades of gray it would seem inefficient to apply a classification method that assigns a single value to each of four classes and all other values to the fifth. Why bother to make a map at all if this is the result? In response to this general guideline, one of the default choices offered by most computer mapping packages for grouping numerical data into classes is to specify equal frequency of values in each class. This classification method is termed *quantiles*, breaking quantities into tiles or groups of equal number. For four classes, the specific term is quartiles, for five classes quintiles, etc. Quantile classification is a trivial classification method to implement (perhaps the real reason it is offered in most packages). The procedure is simply to rank order the values then divide by the number of classes and round up or down to the nearest integer. The result is the number of values in each class. The lowest or highest category is usually assigned any odd number of values that result if the total is not evenly divisible by the number of classes selected.

How does the quantile method fare with our risk index data? Assume that we want 4 classes. With 24 values, this results in 6 values per class. Figure 3.07 shows the risk index values in rank order with the resulting class break points indicated. There are some clear problems. Identical values end up in different classes (and are symbolized differently) and dissimilar values are grouped together. Slight adjustments of the derived class breaks can improve the situation somewhat (e.g., imposing a rule against separating identical values). The map that results (Figure 3.08) presents a pleasing picture with good visual contrast — but an inaccurate one. While it shows us approximately the quarter of the areas at most risk, at least risk, etc., the visual impression would cause the reader to incorrectly assume that the Arizona-New Mexico Plateau

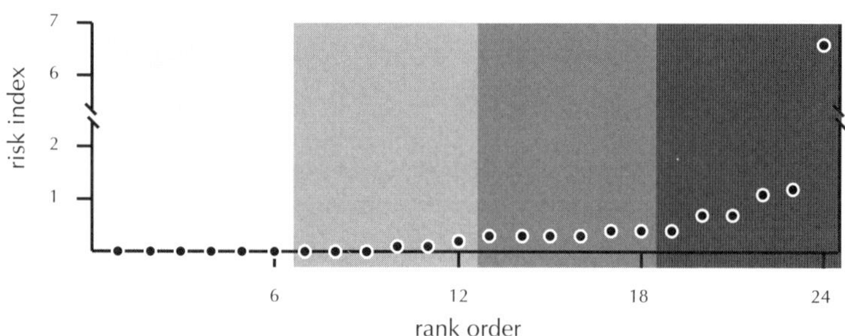


***Figure 3.07*** *The risk index values in rank order with the resulting class break points indicated.*

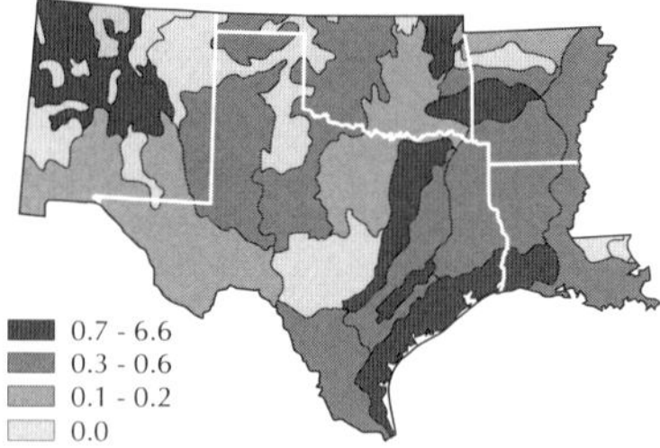


***Figure 3.08*** *Map of risk indices using adjusted quantile classes.*

had a similar risk to the Texas Blackland Prairies and that the a swath from Northeast Oklahoma to Southern Texas was at consistently high risk.

For any skewed data, quantiles are a disaster for a presentation map! It should be clear from our example that the often stated guideline of having a similar number of values in each class is at odds with an equally often stated goal of accurate maps. There seems to be little reason, other than (bad) habit, to use quantiles (except when faced with the problem of comparing maps of different variables or maps of one variable at different times, as discussed below).

A second default classification method offered by most mapping systems is called *equal intervals*. Rather than keeping frequency of values in each class the same, we can keep the range of values (i.e., class intervals) constant by dividing the range of data into equal value steps [e.g., 0-100, 100-200, 200-300, etc.]. Once you have decided how many classes to group data into, you simply determine the range of values (by subtracting the lowest from the highest value), divide by the number of categories desired, and successively add this value to the lowest value to determine the category breaks. For our risk index example, the range is 6.6-0.0 = 6.6. Again we will specify a four-class map. Dividing the overall range by four results in a range for each class of 1.65. The lowest risk index is zero. Category one is thus defined as 0-1.65, category two as 1.70-3.30, category three as 3.35-4.95, and category four as 5.00-6.65.

The result of imposing these categories is illustrated with the rank ordered graph (Figure 3.09, page 48) and map (Figure 3.10, page 48) that result. The map changes dramatically. This time we get the more correct impression of many similar low values and one high value. And, the situation looks less alarming. In spite of the improvement, when we consider the ranked graph and associated class break points, it is clear that some problems remain. The biggest problem is that we end up with a two class map that provides almost no information. We still have situations in which rather different values are lumped together (although this tendency is much less severe than with quantiles) and there are two unused categories. In other applications of equal intervals, we are just as likely to separate similar values into different classes. For example, if equal intervals were calculated for the region 6 risk

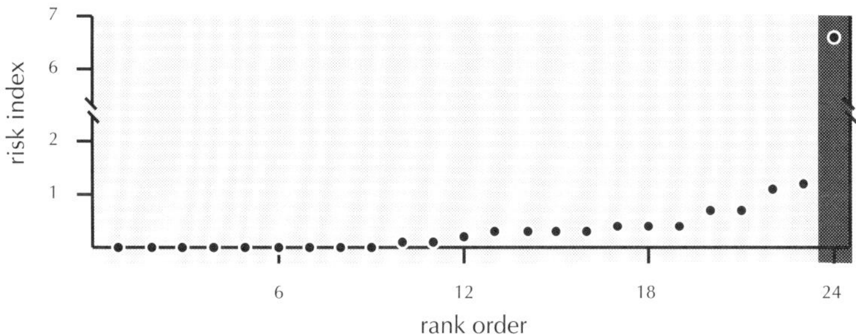


*Figure 3.09* *Equal interval classes.*

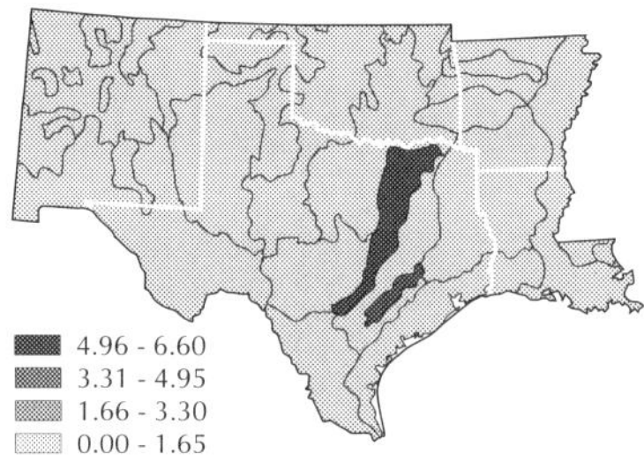


*Figure 3.10* *Map of risk indices using equal interval classes.*

index related to POTW discharge to surface waters, the nearly identical indices of 0.6 and 0.7 would end up in different classes.

Classification by equal intervals is justifiable for many applications. It has the advantage of easy interpretation by map readers (the numerical difference between regions in classes one and two is the same as that between classes three and four). If an isoline map is to be produced (rather than a choropleth map), the spacing between resulting isolines will indicate slope or rate of change on the surface depicted. This makes equal intervals a good classification method for data concerning topics such as atmospheric pollutants for which samples at points are generally used to derive isolines. In situations where values represent areal units, however, we can often do better than equal intervals. When a choropleth map is used for presentation purposes, we usually want both the overall impression and the information about each areal unit to be communicated accurately.

In both of the first two methods considered (quantiles and equal intervals), the classification procedure is an arbitrary one. No consideration at all is given to the data distribution. We can arrive at somewhat more meaningful categories, or at least more accurate reflections of the data, if we define data classes on the basis of some characteristic of the whole data distribution. It is, therefore, a good strategy to begin our classification method selection procedure by graphing the data. A cumulative frequency graph is generally the best approach. In this procedure, ranked data values are plotted on one axis and the number of units (or the cumulative sum of their areas) are plotted on the other axis. Any point on the graph, then, shows the number of units having a specific value or less (or the area of the map with a specific value or less). Unless units vary widely in size the graph will look similar, with the cumulative number of units or their area as the x-axis. Our risk index values are plotted as a cumulative frequency graph by number of units (Figure 3.11).

If the data are skewed (i.e., the cumulative frequency graph results in a curved plot as depicted in Figure 3.11), one approach to selecting class break points is to base data categories on some mathematical progression that reflects the curve's shape. The progression can increase or decrease at a constant rate, at an increasing rate, or at a decreasing rate depending on the shape of the plot. For the risk index data, a mathematical progression that increases at an increasing rate appears appropriate. A geometric progression with class ranges increasing from 0.2 for the lowest class, to 0.4, 1.2, and 4.8 for the highest class reflects the actual values more faithfully than did the equal value step classification

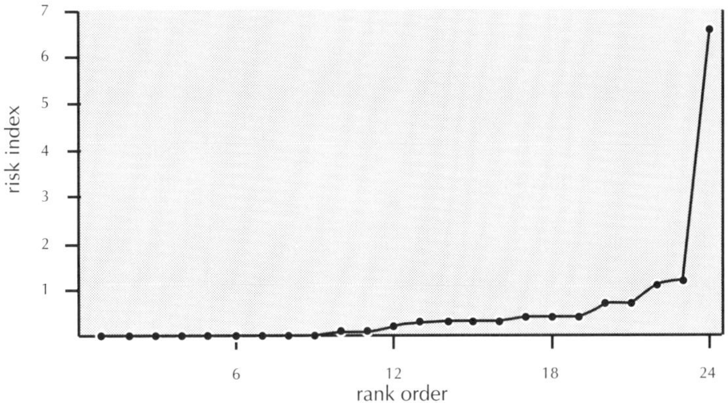


***Figure 3.11*** *Cumulative frequency plot of ranked risk index totals for physical degradation of terrestrial ecosystems/habitat due to urban sources.*

described above (Figure 3.12). The resulting map (Figure 3.13) is more similar to the equal interval map than to the quantile map in isolating the single high value in a separate class. It is distinctly different, however, in depicting variability throughout the rest of the region.

The underlying purpose for using mathematical progressions is a desire to represent the data more accurately than is possible with completely arbitrary procedures such as equal intervals or quantiles. This goal can be stated more formally as: *minimization of variation within classes and maximization of variation between classes*. In other words, we want any given class (for which all members are depicted with identical symbols) to contain values that are as similar as possible and different classes (that are symbolized differently) to be as different as possible.

When, as is typical, the cumulative frequency plot does not produce a nice smooth curve, no mathematical progression will precisely meet the above goal. Our risk index represents such a case. If we want both the overall pattern and individual areas to be depicted accurately, two choices remain. One is to use human visualization

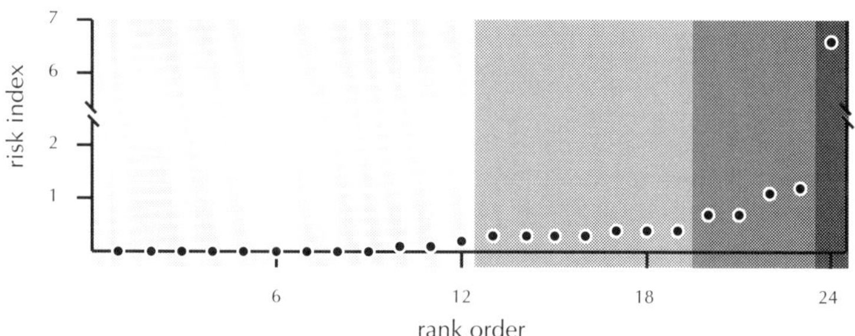


*Figure 3.12* Geometric progression classes.

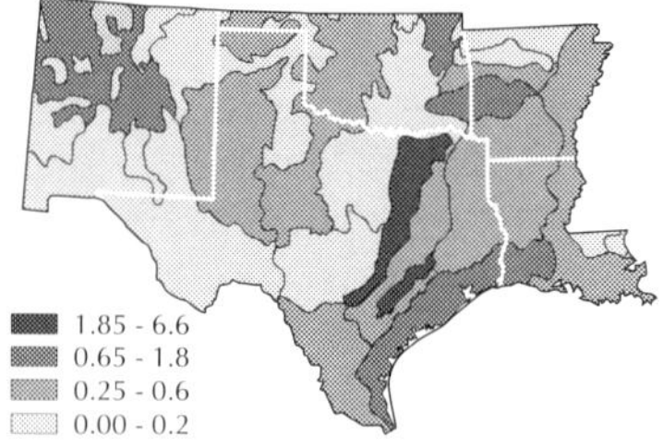


*Figure 3.13* Map of risk indices using geometric progression classes.

skills to examine the graph. To meet the goal of keeping similar values together, we want to be sure not to place class breaks between data values for which the graph's slope is close to zero (e.g., as the quantile and geometric progression classification both did with low risk values). To meet the complementary goal of placing different values in different categories, we look for "natural breaks" — places in the graph where there is a sudden jump in the y-direction. For our risk index data, the natural breaks are between the risk indices of 0.4 and 0.7, between 0.7 and 1.1, and between 1.2 and 6.6. The resultant map is similar to that based on geometric progression classes with less distinction among the very low values and more among the moderate values (Figure 3.14).

The alternative to relying on the vagaries of individual visualization skills, particularly with ambiguous situations or large data sets, is to apply our criterion literally and actually measure the variance within and between categories. Jenks (1977) produced a computer program that uses an iterative (or repeated trials) procedure to calculate these values for different possible class breaks and determine the best one. For this reason his procedure has been called *statistically optimal* data classification.[4] It makes what we can do with a cumulative frequency graph easier and produces more consistent results. For our risk index data, optimal class breaks result in a map similar to that produced using natural breaks. The main difference is a slight shift in regions from low to middle categories (Figure 3.15).

The added advantage of Jenks' procedure is that it provides an accuracy assessment for the optimal class breaks determined for a specific number of classes. If we were to compare this accuracy

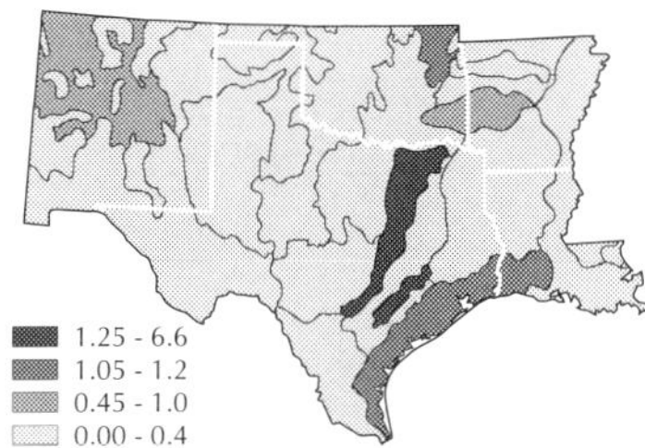


***Figure 3.14*** *Map of risk indices using natural break classes.*

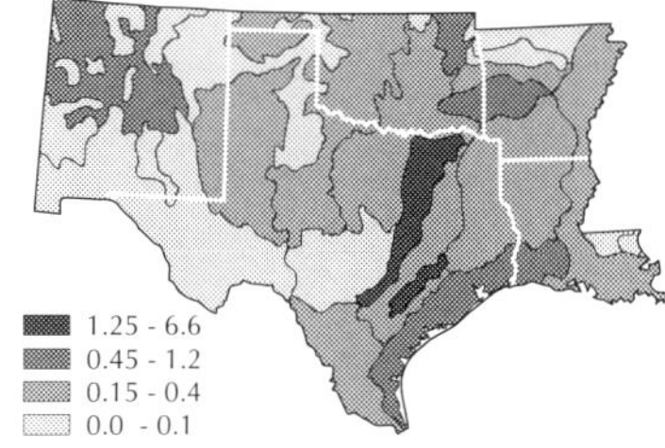


***Figure 3.15*** *Map of risk indices using optimal class breaks.*

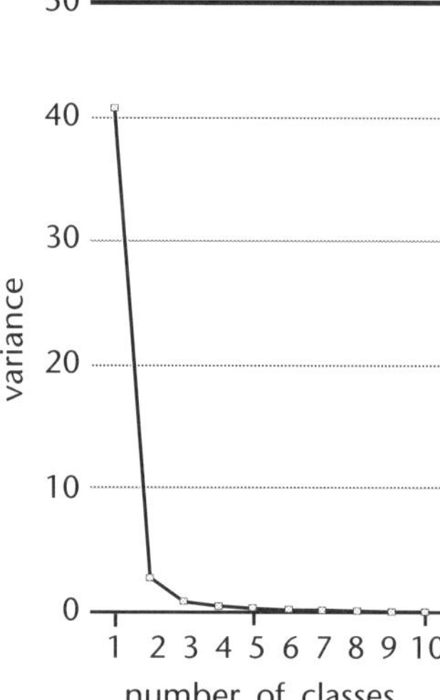


*Figure 3.16* *Accuracy indices for increasing numbers of classes.*

assessment for two through ten classes by plotting the values, we would obtain a picture of how much improvement in accuracy we get with each additional class (Figure 3.16). This plot can be used to determine the ideal number of classes. It will generally start out as a steep curve, then level off. It is at this point that additional classes provide marginal returns (in terms of increased accuracy). For our risk data, a five class map is only marginally better than a four class map. There is little reason to make the map reader's task more difficult by using five rather than four categories.

Although Jenks' (1977) approach to classification has been labeled 'optimal,' it is optimal only in the limited sense of minimizing numerical variation within categories and maximizing variation between them. Not taken into account are two additional issues: the spatial proximity of values and unique problems encountered when comparison of multiple variables for one place or one variable for multiple times are required.

Jenks' procedure is an aspatial one. It does not incorporate any information about spatial proximity. If the goal of map use is to identify regions, rather than simply to identify locations with similar data values, a grouping procedure that emphasizes contiguity of places with similar values is advisable. Evans (1977) discusses the issue of contiguity weighting for data classification and more recently MacDougall (1992) implemented a clustering procedure that groups data values that are both similar and proximate. An alternative for exploratory analysis is to start with a statistically optimal depiction but make use of interactive classification tools (of the sort proposed by Ferreia and Wiggins 1990) to adjust the bounds of categories in a search for spatial pattern.

Whether Jenks' optimization or some form of spatially constrained clustering (that might be optimal in terms of a different standard) is used, resulting maps can be hard to compare. The problem is that both procedures use characteristics of the specific data set to determine class breaks. As a result the class breaks determined (while reflecting the data well) will be unique to the data set and offer no standard for comparison to other data sets. If a time series of maps for one variable is needed, Jenks' method can, of course, be applied to the entire data range. If values change appreciably from year to year, however, the result is likely to be a series of one class maps (with perhaps all values for early years falling in the lowest overall category and all values for the most recent year in the highest). When multiple variables are to be compared, no single overall classification is possible (without transforming all data into some abstract units that are hard to interpret). If applied individually to each of several data sets, Jenks' procedure can make similar values from map to map look different or the reverse. For example, in the case of a normally distributed data variable, the middle category of a five-class map will bound the mean while the middle category of a skewed distribution might represent the low or the high end of the range (depending on direction of skew). "Average" values on one map will be visually paired with low (or high) values on the other map.

For exploratory comparison (either across variables or over time) the best procedure is probably not to class data at all – but to use n-class maps. Although comparisons are likely to be most accurate with n-class maps, the constraints of quantiles and equal intervals (that were criticized above) can also be used to advantage in highlighting particular aspects of difference from one map to another. As an example, consider a time series of maps depicting monthly concentrations of dissolved inorganic nitrogen in Chesapeake Bay (from which the map on the cover represents one time slice). If data are represented by quantiles, a stable pattern from map to map would indicate that the spatial pattern of their rank order is consistent over time (although magnitudes might change from month to month). The stability of pattern (or lack of it) would be particularly apparent if the maps are 'played' as an animation. Similarly, if the same data were then depicted with equal intervals, changes in the amount of the map in different categories would indicate temporal variation in skewness of the data. For example, comparable percentages of the map in each of five categories would indicate a linear frequency distribution of low to high concentrations while a change to a few dark areas on a mostly light map would indicated a spatial concentration that might be due to an isolated point pollution source.

In any comparison for which the mean value of each variable (or each time period) is considered to be a viable standard for comparison, an alternative classification scheme called nested means becomes reasonable. With nested means, the overall mean value of the data set is used as an initial break point. If more than two categories are desired (as they usually are), the sub-mean of each of these categories becomes an additional break point (with further division by subsequent sub-means possible). One limitation of this method is that the mean is not an accurate measure of central tendency for skewed data. A second limitation is that the number of classes is limited to powers of two (e.g., 2, 4, 8, 16, etc.). These drawbacks limit the usefulness of nested means for individual maps. For comparison across variables or over time, however, use of the mean (for unskewed or only moderately skewed data) provides a generally accepted standard measure to 'anchor' the comparisons, thus making them more interpretable.

## Matching Symbols to Referents

Once abstraction choices have been made concerning display type (i.e., image-graphic) and classification method, the next step for the map designer is to translate the categories into appropriate cartographic language. As indicated in chapter two, a key aspect of this process is to match the contrast within and among graphic variables to contrast within and among categories of features mapped.[5]

When our goal is to represent ordered (or numerical) information, several choices of graphic variables are available. Refering back to

Figure 2.28, location, size, focus, color value, and color saturation are all cited as good for depicting ordered data. Focus probably has limited ability to depict order and is best restricted to depiction of data uncertainty. With location on an image, order is implicit and cannot be manipulated. On most maps, this is true as well. In Figure 2.26, for example, the order (in both time and space) of locations affected by the oil spill would be apparent even without the temporal glyphs. On a graphic, location can be more freely manipulated to indicate the order of any variable. On maps we are left with three graphic variables that are particularly well suited to symbolizing order within map categories: size, color value, and color saturation. Although color hue, texture, and orientation all have limited abilities to show order as well, they are probably most effective as redundant cues combined with size, value, or saturation to enhance the impression of order and/or to increase visual contrast among categories.

If asked which oil refinery on the map in Figure 3.17 is the largest, or which county shown in Figure 3.18 has the highest lung cancer incidence, few readers would pick anything other than B and A, respectively. When appropriate graphic variables are used and assigned in a logical way, order becomes intuitively obvious. After deciding which graphic variable to use, therefore, the choice of specific variations of that graphic variable to match variations in the data is relatively straightforward. Larger symbols imply larger data values or more importance. Darker symbols suggest the same thing (if the map's background is white).[6]

If nominal rather than ordinal distinctions are to be represented, we look to a different set of graphic variables. Color hue, texture, orientation, and shape are the best choices. Selection among them

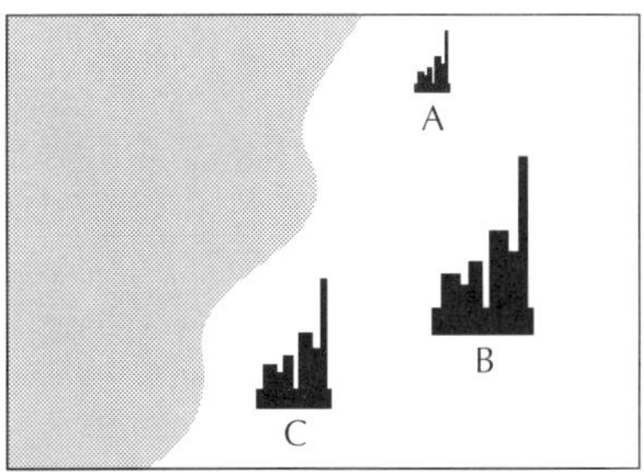

*Figure 3.17*

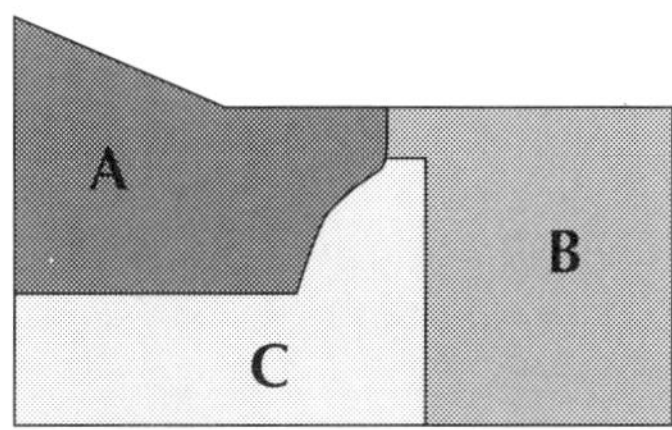


*Figure 3.18*

will depend on whether color hue is available (via a color computer monitor or color printing) and on the relative importance of recognizability of categories versus visual differentiation or isolation. In contrast to the above examples, assignment of symbols within categories is not a simple matter for nominal distinctions due to the wide range of symbol variation choices, the often non-visual concepts to be communicated, and the lack of an intuitive logic such as bigger equals more. If asked where the oil refineries, fertilizer manufacurers, chemical processing plants, and uranium enrichment facilities are, the answer is not intuitively obvious from the map in Figure 3.19. On a map to depict county level opinion about whether nuclear waste, water pollution, air pollution, or radon is the most critical environmental threat, similar difficulty in matching symbols with referents is encountered (Figure 3.20). These nominal concepts are more complicated than the concept of "order." The examples shown in Figures 3.19 and 3.20 depict differences in kind of thing, as they should for nominal data, but do so with very abstract symbols that require memorization of (or constant referal to) the category definitions.

## Mimetic Versus Abstract Symbols

Just as an overall display can vary in abstractness from images to graphics, symbols embedded within the display also have a range of abstractness. We can identify a symbol abstractness continuum from *mimetic* to *abstract* (Figure 3.21). At one extreme, mimetic symbols look like the phenomenon being depicted. At an intermediate point on the continuum are symbols that bring to mind the phenomenon through a widely learned association between a symbol and referent (e.g., a star means something important) or a logical association implied by a shared visual or conceptual attribute (e.g., both symbol and phenomenon are dominantly green or arranged in a regular pattern). The most abstract symbols, while distinguishable from one another, have only arbitrary assignments to the referents they represent (e.g., a triangle for a water well and a square for an oil well). As with the image to graphic continuum, symbols from the entire mimetic to abstract range have advantages in specific situations. Although they take more effort to identify and remember, abstract symbols can be very discriminable. A reader can, therefore, quickly identify differences while scanning from place to place on a map. Abstract symbols are probably best

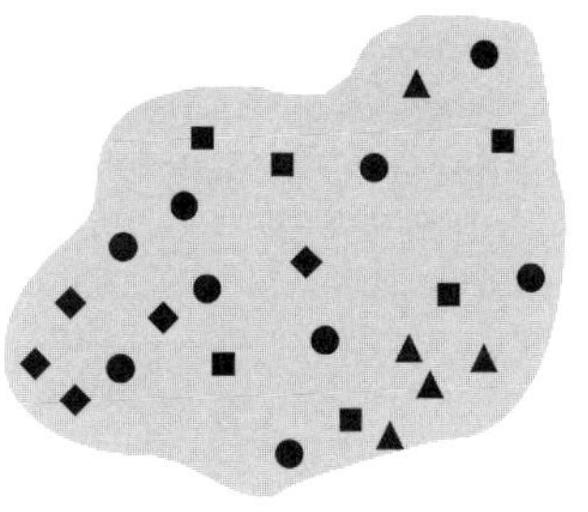

*Figure 3.19 Where are the refineries?*

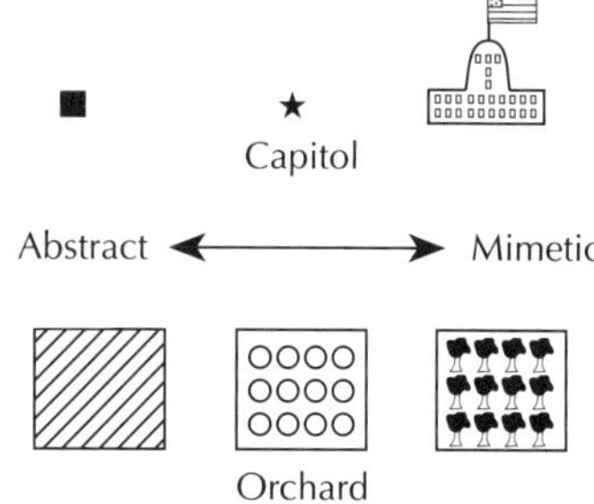


*Figure 3.21 Symbol Abstractness.*

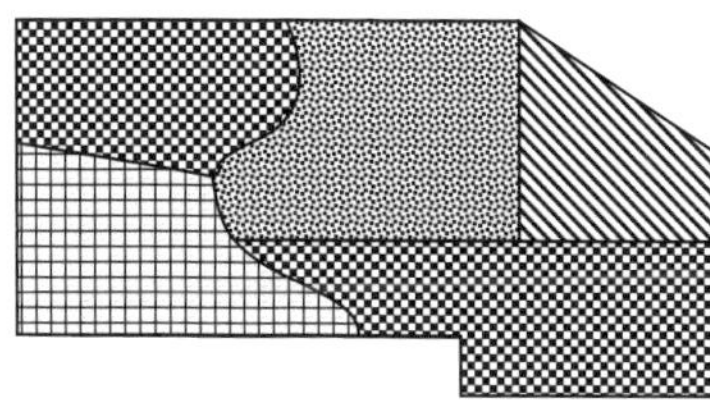

*Figure 3.20 For which area is water pollution is the biggest threat?*

suited to use by analysts at the exploratory end of our analysis-decision-making cycle. An analyst who is intent on identifying unknown patterns and relationships will take the time to learn the abstract symbol-referent relationships. On the other hand, for communication purposes, particularly to a non-specialist audience, mimetic symbols are preferred. The non-specialist will spend less time perusing a map and requires more obvious cues to the features depicted.

## Selecting a Data Model for Quantities Aggregated to Units[7]

Many analysts and map users disregard the differences between data and the phenomena they represent. This problem is particularly true for data aggregated to unit areas (e.g., counties, census tracts, ecoregions, etc.). As a result, the greatest potential for misinterpretation of quantitative environmental data is when data aggregated to areas are mapped. The misinterpretation is due to the assumption that, if data have been collected or organized by areal unit, the areal units must be relevant to the phenomenon that the data represent. This assumption is often inappropriate. For this reason, we will focus on the issue of selecting an appropriate symbol type to represent aggregate areal data. Much of the discussion, however, can be extended to symbolization choices for other numerical data (e.g., pollution sampled at points).

The choice of symbols for representing quantities aggregated to areal units (e.g., birth rates per county, risk indicies for ecoregions) is difficult due to the range of options available. Maps using dot, graduated symbol, choropleth, isopleth, fishnet, prism, dasymetric, and plastic shading symbolization have been applied. In spite of this range, many computer environments provide only one option — the choropleth map. To fully understand the constraints and bias that this limitation places on the analyst (and to see why it is worth exporting data from the GIS to a more flexible mapping package) we need to consider the concept of a *data model.* As Jenks (1967) described when he introduced this concept to cartography three decades ago, a data model is an abstract representation, in graphic and/or mathematical form, of the key spatial features of the phenomenon that the data represent.

Quantities aggregated to units such as counties can represent phenomena with a considerable range of spatial continuity (Hsu 1979). A range from discrete to continuous is possible for both stepped and smooth functions. A discrete phenomenon is one which occurs at isolated places separated by areas for which the phenomenon is not present (e.g., tons of toxic waste generated per county may be recorded on a county unit basis but will be generated and stored at a limited number of sites within the county). If the distribution can be conceived as discrete (discontinuous) at the intended map scale, the designer should not select symbols which imply a continuous surface (i.e., do not use isolines). If, on the other hand, the phenomenon is continuous across space, discrete point symbols that vary in size (e.g., graduated circles) would be inappropriate.

In addition to considering where a phenomenon fits on the discrete-continuous range, the character of variation in the phenomenon across space must be considered. Some phenomena (e.g., tax rates) can vary quite abruptly as political boundaries are crossed while others (e.g., gallons of ground water pumped for irrigation per county) can exhibit a relatively smooth variation quite independent of the units to which data are aggregated. To determine whether spatial variation for the phenomenon being mapped is abrupt or smooth (or at an intermediate level) we must determine whether values associated with adjacent areal units are independent or interdependent. The more independent the values, the more abrupt the variation will be. If we consider the character of variation together with the nature of the distribution, a phenomena space results (Figure 3.22), locations in which can be represented by a set of graphic data models (Figure 3.23). When we try to represent these data models with 2D symbols, we end up with a similar matrix of symbol choices that are appropriate for phenomena at specific locations in the phenomena space (Figure 3.24, page 60).

Even with this system for matching spatial phenomena to appropriate abstract representation forms, the matching of symbols to referents remains a somewhat subjective endeavor. Determining

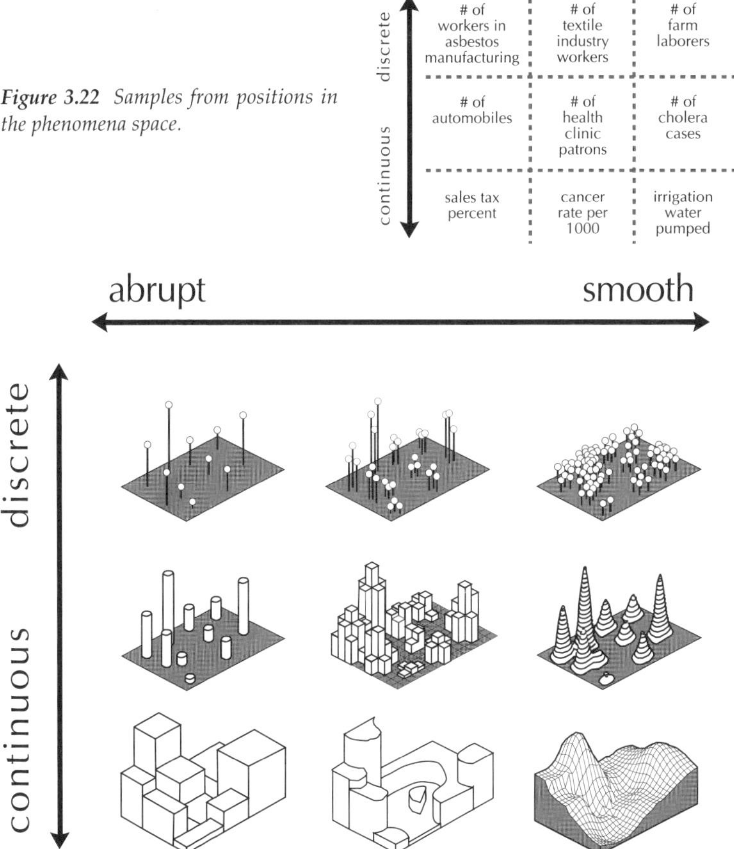


***Figure 3.22*** *Samples from positions in the phenomena space.*

***Figure 3.23*** *Sample data models to represent the phenomena space defined by spatial continuity and character of variation. Reproduced from MacEachren (1992) with permission.*

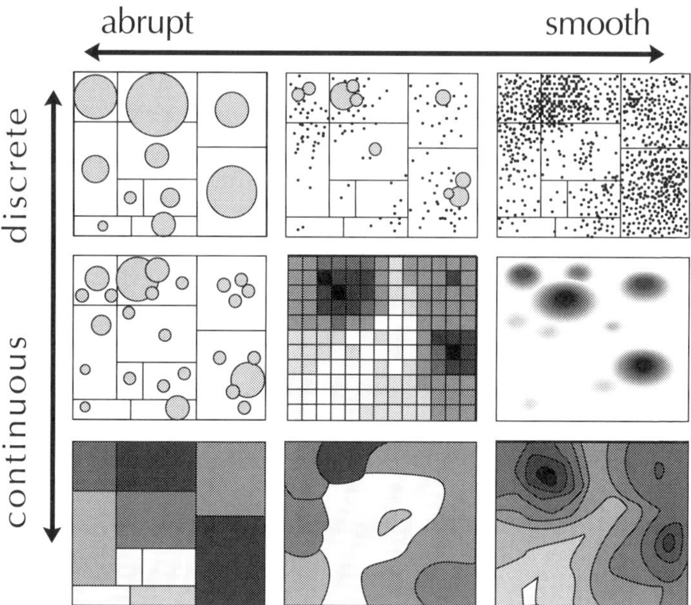


*Figure 3.24* Matching map types to data models. Reproduced from MacEachren (1992) with permission.

how discrete or continuous or how abrupt or smooth a particular phenomenon is must rely on expert knowledge combined with an understanding of the objectives for analysis and/or presentation. In addition, questions of relative emphasis on position versus areal extent, or data magnitudes versus change in magnitude over distance, become secondary considerations that help in selecting between symbolization methods that reflect similar underlying data models.

The arrangement of map types derived by linking each to a phenomenon type can be considered a kind of map syntactics (i.e., a logic for structuring related map types). The details of the syntactics were worked out in the context of a particular map symbolization problem — how to depict the disease AIDS on a series of animated state-level maps when the highest resolution data any state would release was county level. Most maps of AIDS incidence produced from county data had been choropleth maps. This is perhaps because of a mistaken idea that a choropleth map is the most accurate representation of data by county (or simply because choropleth maps are easy to produce with a number of readily available microcomputer mapping packages). With AIDS, it was clear that cases were not evenly distributed within each county. Although a choropleth map would accurately represent the data, then, it would not be an accurate reflection of the phenomenon that the data represent.

Since a choropleth map was clearly a bad choice for representing AIDS, other options were considered, beginning with the remaining three most common symbolization methods for quantities on small-scale maps: graduated circle, dot, and isopleth maps (Figure 3.25). Graduated circle maps would depict the county data accurately and would not imply a homogeneous spatial distribution within counties (as would a choropleth map). They would, however, provide no information about spatial distribution below the county level (at best) or suggest tightly clustered concentrations of AIDS incidence (at worst). Dot maps share the advantage of retaining an accurate depiction of numbers per county while providing the chance to represent known spatial variability within each county. With AIDS incidence, however, dot maps suggest a spatial independence that did not seem warranted. The client for the maps being produced, Peter Gould, felt that the phenomenon of AIDS was most accurately modeled as both continuous and smooth (that there is a spatial dependence at work). Gould, therefore, opted for

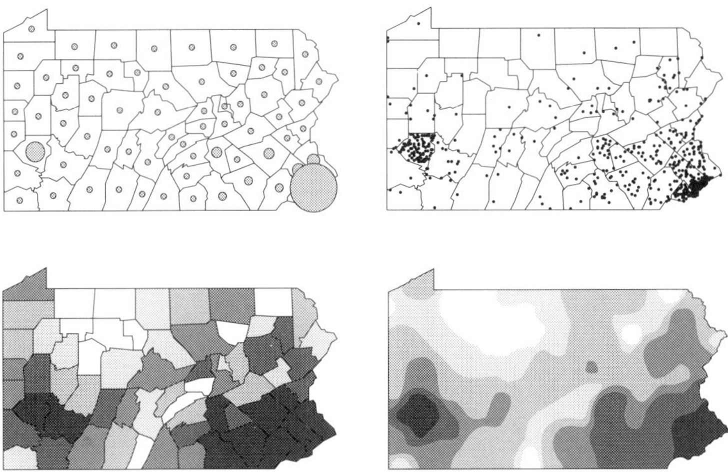

**Figure 3.25** *Representing the distribution of AIDS cases as abrupt/discrete (graduated circle map–top left), abrupt/continuous (choropleth map–bottom left), smooth/discrete (dot map–top right), and smooth/continuous (isopleth map–bottom right).*

isoplethic representation to match his spatial model of the disease (see Gould, et al. 1991, and Gould 1993 for discussion of the spatial aspects of the AIDS epidemic and Gould, et al. 1990 for some of the initial color maps generated representing spread of the disease over time).

The choice of isopleth maps for AIDS incidence data is certainly less wrong than choosing any of the other three standard symbolization methods. If the disease was influenza or measles, typical contagious diseases, the smooth-continuous distribution model underlying isopleth maps would be an excellent match. For AIDS, however, with its more limited means of transmission, a symbolization form with at least some indication of discontinuity seems warranted. Perhaps the most accurate depiction is the middle model on the far right of the phenomena space of Figure 3.23. This symbol form was actually selected by Gould (1989) for his map of AIDS in the U.S. as a whole (Figure 3.26). A case can be made, however, that AIDS is neither as continuous in its distribution as an isopleth map implies *nor* as smooth. Due to the transmission mechanisms for the disease,

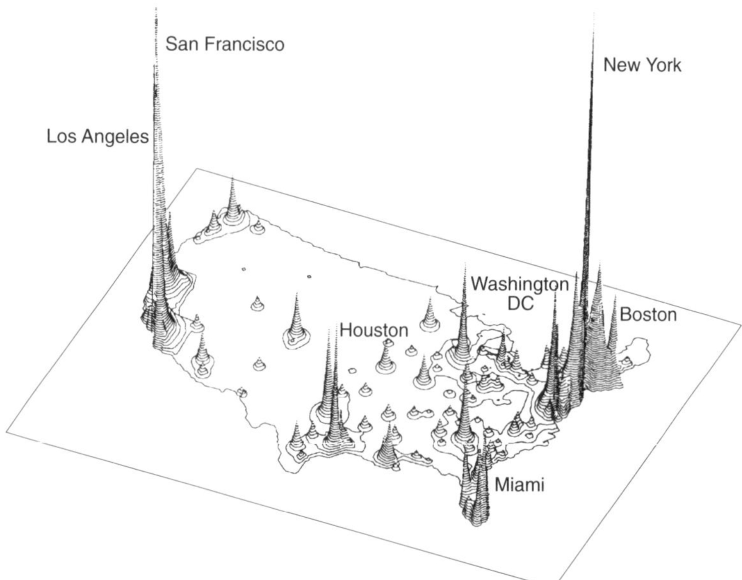


***Figure 3.26*** *Estimated distribution of diagnosed AIDS infection in the contiguous United States, July 18, 1988. This map is based on data for major cities and is reproduced from Gould (1989) with permission.*

spatial dependence is not as strong as for influenza or measles. A middle position of the phenomenon space (called a chorodot map) has been suggested as being the most accurate model, at least for representing data collected at a county level (MacEachren and DiBiase 1991) (Figure 3.27).

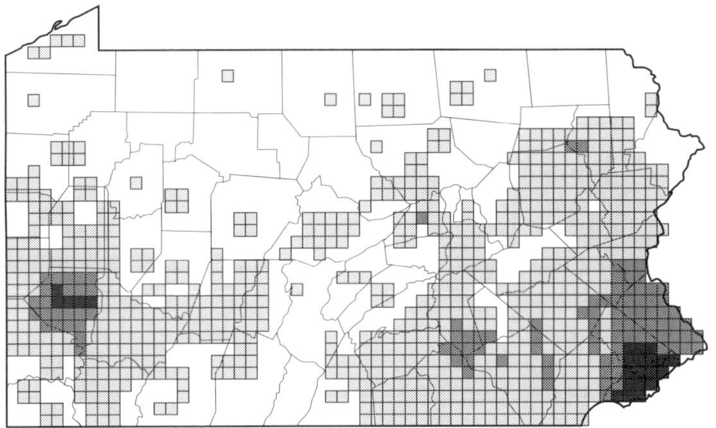

***Figure 3.27*** *A prototype application of the "chorodot" technique used for the 1988 AIDS data. This technique depicts values in each county with uniform grid cells shaded to depict one case (light gray), 8 cases (medium gray), or 64 cases (dark gray).*

## Summary

The chapter has focused on how we link the cartographic language delineated in Chapter 2 to phenomena in the real world that we want to investigate or present. This linking of symbol to referent is a process of abstraction that includes several interrelated decisions. We make a variety of determinations about the nature of the phenomena to be represented and about whether our representation goals demand realism or interpretation.

The abstraction process begins with identifying the spatial dimensionality and level of measurement discussed in the previous chapter. Decisions must then be made about how to employ our graphic variables to best advantage. The way these variables are used will differ for images, where they allow a viewer or analyst to determine what features are being depicted, to graphics, where the viewer or analyst is trying to identify specific relationships between the features symbolized. In the latter case, the viewer presumably already knows what she or he should focus on and needs display tools that bring these features to the fore while at the same time suppressing or removing unnecessary detail. As we move from images toward graphics, the importance of classification systems that group phenomenon into manageable categories increases. Along this same continuum, the link between graphic variables and their referents usually becomes more abstract (e.g., with color hue and value used in images to mimic real world appearance but used in graphics to represent categories that may or may not even be visible). For presentation uses, we often try to make our representations somewhat less abstract for the lay viewer by using mimetic symbols (that look like the features they depict) on an otherwise abstract map base (that has little similarity to the environment represented). When the topic to be depicted is quantitative, a further abstraction decision is required. Quantitative spatial information is generally encoded as samples at points or aggregates over areas. In both cases, some model of the real phenomenon that the data represent must be adopted in order to select an appropriate representation method. Questions of the degree of continuity across space and the kind of spatial variability are critical to this abstraction decision.

## Endnotes

[1]*Tobler (1973) seems to be the first among modern cartographers to argue for unclassed choropleth maps as analytical tools.*

[2]*A comprehensive review of data classification appears in Evans (1977). Here, a few of the most common techniques will be compared.*

[3]*MAC Choro, a Macintosh mapping package also supports n-class maps for exploratory analysis -- maps in which data are unclassed and area fills are directly proportional to each data value as in Figure 3.03. An n-class map provides the most accurate possible representation of the data, but often a rather noisy picture with low contrast.*

[4]*Richard Groop, of Michigan State University has produced a version of this program that runs on IBM PC and compatible computers (Groop 1980). A Macintosh version, called Classit, has also been developed by Barbara Buttenfield at SUNY–Buffalo. Both authors have provided copies of their software, and their assistance is appreciated.*

[5]*In this section a variety of guidelines will be presented for matching symbols to data. The assumption here is that the matching will be consciously done by the map designer. To facilitate map use by those not familiar with cartographic guidelines, a number of researchers have advocated incorporation of guidelines in expert systems. See Weibel and Buttenfield*

*(1988), Muller and Zeshen (1990), and Hutzler and Spiess (1993) for discussion of the issues involved.*

[6]*Recent research by McGranaghan (1989) indicates that with non-black backgrounds, there is considerably less consistency among map viewers about whether dark or light intuitively implies more. Particularly with gray backgrounds, individuals were not even consistent with themselves (sometimes they judged light areas to mean more, but elsewhere they judged dark areas as more).*

[7]*The following section is excerpted from MacEachren and DiBiase (1991) Animated maps of aggregated data: Conceptual and practical problems, C&GIS, 18(4):221-229.*

# 4

# Visualization Quality and the Representation of Uncertainty

*Visualization quality and the representation of uncertainty in visual displays are interrelated issues at the heart of visual spatial analysis. Visualization quality refers to the veracity of interpretation by a viewer or analyst who has studied a map or other visualization tool. Interpretation veracity will be dependent upon the appropriateness of the abstraction process used to derive the display, the uncertainty inherent in the display, and the viewer's understanding of both that abstraction and uncertainty. Attributes identified for locations and the location of particular attributes can both be uncertain and this uncertainty can change over time. The cartographic literature has largely ignored the question of depicting uncertainty. Insuring viewer understanding of uncertainty, then, will depend on developing a means to represent it.*

## Visualization Quality

The previous chapter dealt with many of the attribute transformations that must be considered when designing visual representation tools to support environmental analysis. With presentation applications, matching the characteristics of the representation method (smooth to abrupt and continuous to discrete) to the characteristics of the phenomenon and categorizing the available information in an appropriate way are critical to avoiding misunderstanding. For exploratory analysis, however, attempting to find the one symbol-referent relationship that seems most correct may be a mistake. Instead, we should draw on the flexibility of computer tools to interactively manipulate symbol-referent relationships. Such manipulation can lead to insights that would otherwise be missed but should be used cautiously because what we see is not necessarily what it seems.

An analogy to statistical hypothesis testing is helpful to recognize the two kinds of visualization errors that can result when maps and graphics are used as exploratory tools. The analyst must consider the possibility of both Type I and Type II errors, described by MacEachren and Ganter (1990) as "seeing wrong" and "not seeing."

Seeing wrong, or the identification of false patterns or relationships, can occur, for example, when the transformation from the three–dimensional earth to two–dimensional display is not taken into account for continental problems. Wilmont, et al. (1985) provide a particularly relevant example of such a situation. Their example demonstrates the difference in apparent temperature distribution across North America that can result if the 3D to 2D transformation of space is done before interpolating a surface from samples at points rather than after (Figure 4.01). If interpolation from sample points to a continuous surface is done on the sphere, a more accurate depiction of the temperature surface results (with some locations exhibiting as much as a 15° C difference in apparent temperature and a dramatic difference in the pattern of isotherms for the arctic and parts of Central America).

Even with an accurate depiction of the data, based upon spherical interpolation, the chance for seeing wrong (Type I errors) exists if

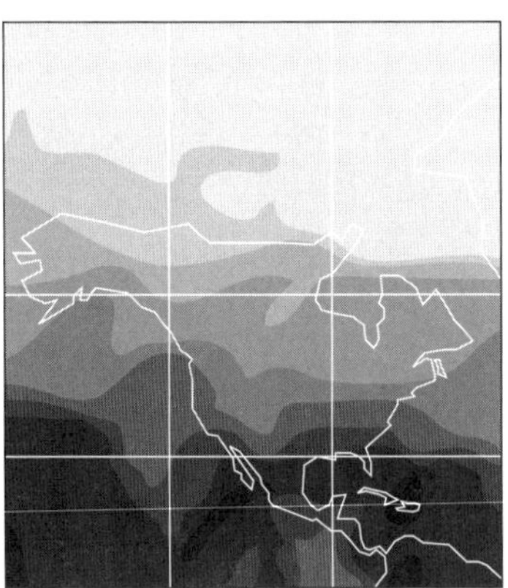

Interpolation before projection

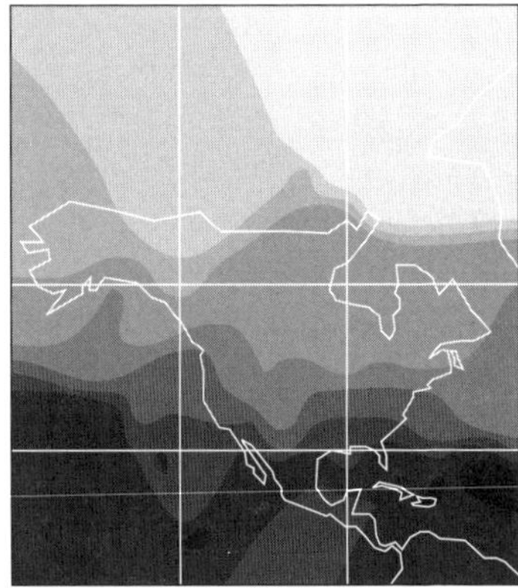

Interpolation after projection

***Figure 4.01*** *This pair of maps represents the distortion in temperature pattern that can result if sample locations of a continuous variable (i.e., temperature) are projected onto a flat map before the isarithmic surface is interpolated. As Wilmont, et al. (1985) have pointed out, the correct procedure is to do interpolation in spherical coordinates, then project the resulting surface to a two-dimensional map. After Wilmont, et al. (1985), Fig. 3, p. 12 and Fig. 4, p. 13.*

the subsequent 3D to 2D transformation is not selected properly. For any analysis in which relative areas are a factor, the map projection used should preserve area. Most climatological maps, however, seem to be produced on a projection that either preserves angular relationships (a feature critical to meteorological forecasts but not to long term climate analysis) or one that is equirectangular (because it is simple to make and use). These projections exaggerate the size of high latitude locations in relation to equatorial ones. A depiction of human induced global warming in the mid-to upper-latitudes, therefore, might suggest a much more dramatic global change than the model really indicates (Figure 4.02, page 70).

As with statistical analysis, visual exploration provides as much chance for Type II as for Type I errors. It is just as likely that an analyst will fail to see a true pattern as to see an illusory one. The issue of how the three-dimensional earth is transformed into a two-dimensional map is just as relevant to Type II as Type I errors. Figure 2.06 provided an example of a situation where a pattern (converging pollutants) might be missed if depicted on a projection that did not show that convergence. Transformations of data (rather than space) can also contribute to Type II interpretation errors. As illustrated in the preceding chapter, data classification procedures can result in considerable differences in apparent pattern for data aggregated to continuous units. MacEachren and Ganter (1990) contrived an extreme example to illustrate the potential for missing an obvious pattern if only one data classification method is considered. When the data in Figure 4.03A (page 71) are depicted with an equal interval classification (Figure 4.03B), the northeast-southwest pattern is barely revealed. An interactive data classification tool of the sort suggested by Ferreira and Wiggins (1990), however, would allow a pattern to appear that suggests a physical connection between Pennsylvania's geologic structure and the data depicted (Figure 4.03C). The fact that the data used in the above example are fictitious should make clear the uncertainty in any such visual analysis. Data exploration tools can allow us to identify potentially meaningful patterns that we might otherwise miss, but these tools can not always determine the probability that the pattern seen is real.

An important issue here is what Muehrcke (1990) has termed "map stability." Map stability refers to the extent to which map appearance changes with slight alterations in how we process or symbol-

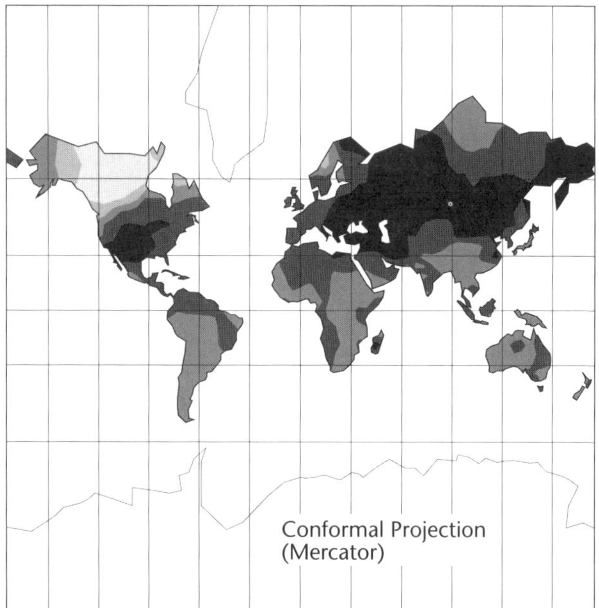


**Mean 1990 Temperature**
**Relative to Long Term Temperature Histories**

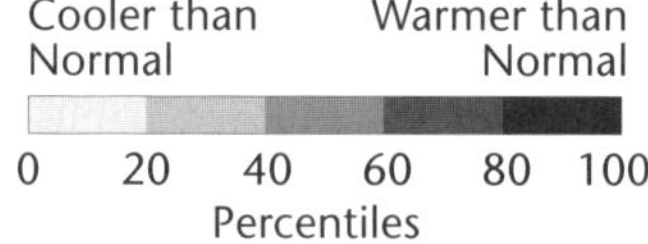


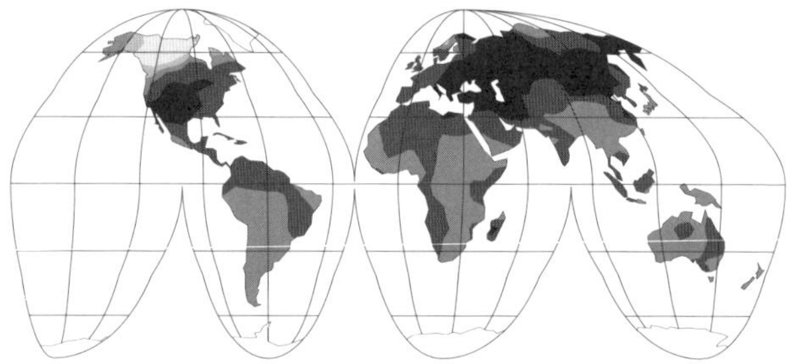

Equal-Area Projection (Goode's)

***Figure 4.02*** *The impact of map projection choice on apparent changes in global temperature. The Mercator projection exaggerates patterns of change in the mid-to upper-latitudes while the Goode's projection depicts regions at their correct proportions, but interrupts oceans to minimize distortion on land.*

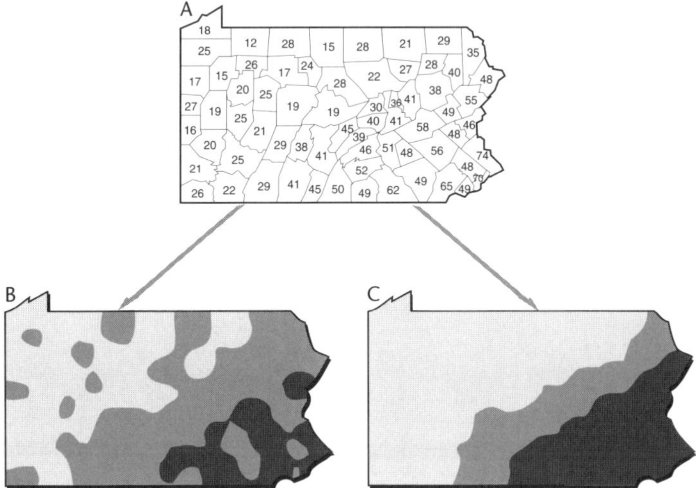


***Figure 4.03*** *Difference in apparent patterns resulting from different data classification procedures. Reproduced from MacEachren and Ganter 1990, Figure 6, p. 77.*

ize data. If the map exhibits little or no change (i.e., is stable) we can be reasonably confident that it is an accurate representation of the phenomenon being depicted. If, on the other hand, instability is revealed by alterations in processing (e.g., as we change data class breaks slightly on a choropleth map), we should be very cautious about accepting any one of the views provided.

A dramatic example of instability, and potential for identifying patterns where none really exist (or missing patterns that do not exist), is provided when we look at some elevation data used to assess GIS database accuracy (MacEachren and Davidson 1987). Consider the two contour maps depicted in Figure 4.04 (page 72). Are these places in similar or different parts of the country? Do they have similar or different drainage patterns and how will the patterns affect runoff of agricultural chemicals from farms? The maps use contours, a relatively abstract form of map symbolization, to depict a three-dimensional surface. These maps illustrate the sensitivity of contour symbolization to the resolution of the underlying data. The maps are of exactly the same place, but generated from elevation samples taken at 50 meter versus 500 meter spacing. If we were to vary the interpolation procedure used to translate the sample values into contours, we could expect significant visual changes in the map at the bottom but only minor changes in the top map. There is a sampling resolution threshold that must be reached before contours can be considered a stable symbolization method (Figure 4.05). This is probably true for any data collected at points that we would represent with isolines (e.g., atmospheric lead concentration, nitrogen concentration in the Chesapeake Bay, etc.). Interestingly, if we portray the same two data sets using a perspective (fishnet) map instead of contours, the visual difference is less pronounced (Figure 4.06). This illustration demonstrates that map stability is dependent upon both the data we select to represent the real world and the symbolization method we select to represent those data.

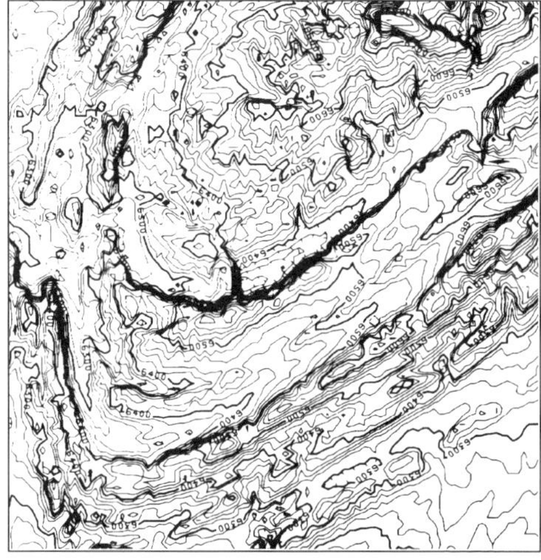


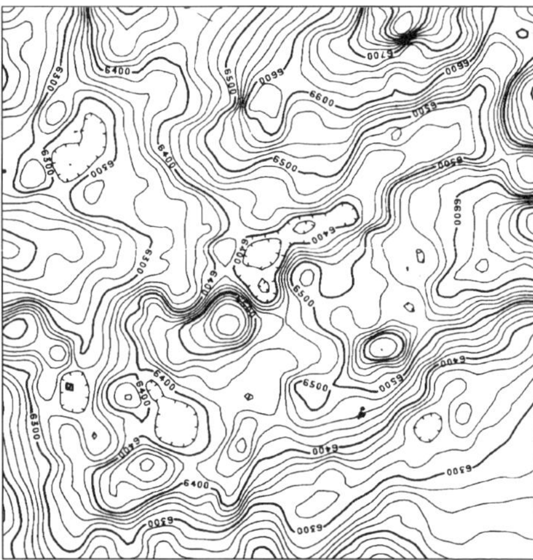


*__Figure 4.04__ Contour maps based on a 50-meter and 500-meter sample, respectively. After MacEachren and Davidson (1987, Fig. 1, p. 300).*

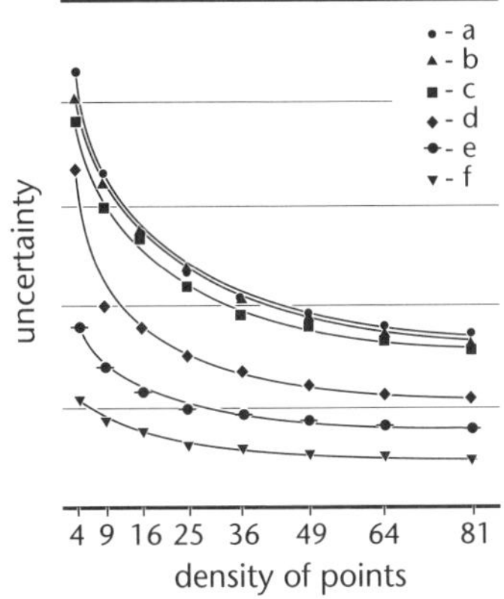


*Figure 4.05 Decreasing uncertainty with increasing density of sample points for six sample terrain surfaces of differing geomorphic character. Density values are number of samples per square kilometer. After MacEachren and Davidson 1987, Fig. 12, p. 314.*

*Figure 4.06 Perspective views of isometric representations shown in Figure 4.04. Reproduced by permission from MacEachren and Ganter 1990, Fig. 4, p. 73.*

***Particularly at exploratory and confirmatory stages of analysis, rather than trying to pick one best method for symbolization and one best design, multiple views should be generated.*** Multiple views allow us to recognize instability in the symbolization, and at the same time shift emphasis to different aspects of a problem.[1] This shifting emphasis increases our chance to notice critical patterns or relationships. As Muehrcke (1990) points out, GIS makes the examination of multiple views almost as easy as selecting a single view. Patterns that remain stable through such an iterative variation of data processing and symbolization choices can be taken as relatively strong confirmatory evidence that the patterns really exist, while patterns that fluctuate and/or break down during this type of scrutiny should be regarded as much less certain. Particularly during confirmatory stages of analysis, however, we must remain aware of the fact that humans are extremely good at noticing patterns even when they do not exist (e.g., canals on Mars). A stable pattern that we notice, therefore, might be nothing more than our active imaginations. One of the powers of GIS is that we are not restricted to map analysis, or to statistical analysis, or to modeling, but can easily integrate these and other approaches. It is this integrative component of GIS that makes it an ideal platform for "visual thinking".

## Representing Uncertainty[2]

Abstraction is necessary to cope with the complexity of the real world. All abstraction, however, introduces uncertainty into our analysis and policy formulation. Uncertainty about data quality, relationships among variables, and the ability of models to mimic natural processes are critical issues in environmental research and policy formulation. With GIS, uncertainty can be high due to the merging of multiple layers (with different and sometimes unknown quality) and to the potential for both location and attribute uncertainty. We can, however, overcome the tendency of GIS to hide uncertainty by using the integrative tools it provides to directly represent that uncertainty in ways that analysts and policy makers can make sense of.

### Categories of Uncertainty

Map makers have had a concern with uncertainty of spatial information since the first navigation maps were produced. Recently the scope of this concern has been emphasized by the National Center for Geographic Information and Analysis initiative on *Visualization of Data Quality*. Within the cartography and GIS communities, the issue has been largely restricted to "data quality," (defined as incorporating locational and attribute accuracy, logical consistency, and completeness). There is more to the uncertainty inherent in map and graphic depiction. To use a GIS effectively for either scientific inquiry or policy formulation, the scope must be broadened to include other kinds of uncertainty.

The issue of measuring uncertainty in environmental data and analysis has been dealt with elsewhere and will not be repeated here (Morgan and Henrion 1990; Rejeski and Kapuscinski 1990). The distinction between data quality and uncertainty and the categories of uncertainty relevant to GIS-based analysis, however, have been given less attention. A brief example that I recently developed will illustrate the distinction between quality and uncertainty (MacEachren 1992, p. 11-12).

> *Imagine a single census block in a city. You have sent an enumerator out to take the census. In this particular case, the response rate is 90%. In data quality terms, we might say that our population and income information for this*

*block is of less than perfect quality because of the lack of "completeness" in the data. Further, there may be "attribute inaccuracy" in the data collected due to misunderstanding of the survey questions or deliberate misinformation about items such as income or education, or "spatial inaccuracy" due to address coding errors by the census enumerator. If, in the adjacent census block we somehow achieved 100% participation in the census, everyone understood the questions and gave truthful responses, and the enumerator made no mistakes, a* ***data quality*** *assessment would label that unit's data as perfect. What we will be leaving out of this assessment is the issue of variability (over both space and time and within categories). This latter point is made quite forcefully by Langford and Unwin (1991) who argue that, for the mapping of most socio-economic phenomena, a choropleth map of aggregated data for enumeration units is "a poor choice" due to extreme within-unit variability that is the rule rather than the exception.*

*In addition to variability due to spatial aggregation, attribute aggregation adds additional variability, and therefore, uncertainty. All data are categorized. Even when individual measurements are retained in the database, categories will be implicitly defined by the mathematical precision of individual measurements. For example, temperatures might be measured to the nearest degree. Most data in a GIS, however, will be grouped into much broader categories (e.g., soil classifications, income brackets, whether a house has indoor plumbing or not, etc.). In all of these cases, the categorization introduces uncertainty even when the data are of high quality.*

*We can only be certain that a particular location—a particular data object—fits somewhere within the attribute bounds of the categories and the spatial bounds of the enumeration unit to which it is aggregated. The aggregate totals for our census blocks disguise the variability within those census blocks. Our level of uncertainty about map locations will be a function not only of the quality of values (as defined above), but of variance around the mean values we typically use to represent the unit, and of spatial variability across the unit.*

> *In addition to spatial and attribute data quality and variability, a final uncertainty to be dealt with is temporal. The data, even if accurate and homogeneous, represent a snapshot at one point in time. Our uncertainty about their veracity will increase due to uncertainty about temporal information, resolution with which that information is specified, and the difference in time between data collection and data use. The temporally induced uncertainty will vary with kind of phenomena being represented.*
>
> *When we use a GIS, the important issue is quality of the decisions we make—about a research course to follow, an urban development policy to impose, or an environmental regulation to enforce. Whether we use the term data quality or data uncertainty matters less than whether the tool we give the GIS user is adequate for deciding how much faith to put in any particular piece of information extracted from the database.*
>
> *We can have highly accurate data while still having* ***imprecise*** *data. This lack of precision is at least as important an issue as a lack of accuracy. Precision here refers, not only to the specificity of data values in terms of significant digits, but in a more general sense to "the degree of refinement with which an operation is performed or a measurement taken" ([Meriam] Webster's New Collegiate Dictionary, 1974). In this sense it is an assessment of the resolution of categories by which a phenomenon is represented (i.e., categorical precision). Although, mathematically, a population density of 165.34 persons/sq. mi. would be considered precise, spatially it is not if that county is 1000 sq. mi. in size. Also, the map representation of the attribute (population density) loses its attribute categorical precision when the data are aggregated into an attribute category ranging from 50-500 persons/sq. mi. Figure 4.07 provides examples of topics for which map uncertainty is due primarily to accuracy or categorical precision.*

The nature of uncertainty resulting from unknown accuracy or lack of mathematical and/or categorical precision in location, time, or attributes will vary across the image-graphic range discussed in the previous chapter. In both cases uncertainty in time or space can be presented as an annotation to the image in the form of a verbal statement, a map, or a diagram. A map might be used, for example, to show the confidence concerning the ground location of an aerial photograph's principal point (Figure 4.08), or a diagram might depict the certainty about when that photo was taken. Uncertainty about attributes of an image will be confined to their appearance. In an image, there are no symbols representing referents that are

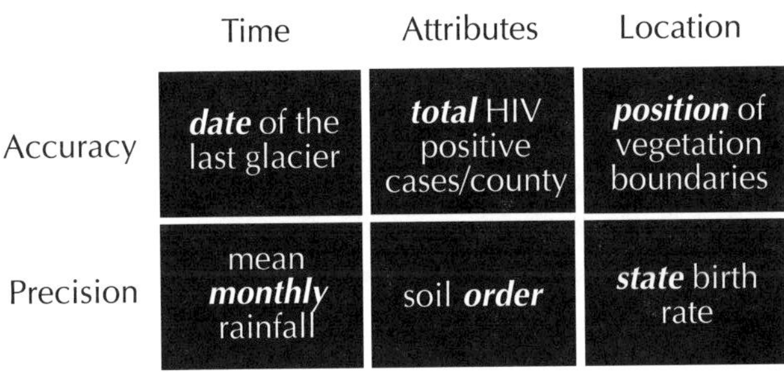


*Figure 4.07* *Examples of topics for which locational, attribute, and temporal accuracy and categorical precision contribute to uncertainty.*

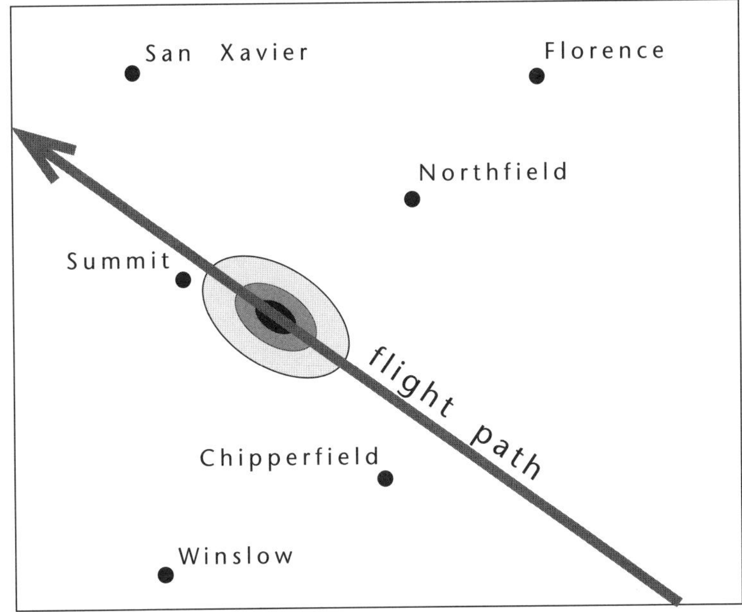


*Figure 4.08* *Equiprobability ellipses indicating the likelihood that the photo's center is on or within the ellipse.*

themselves abstractions (having uncertain reference to the real world). Instead, attributes of color (hue, value, and saturation) depict color of the environment directly. The only graphic variables used in an image, therefore, are color hue, value, and saturation. Although the size, texture, etc. of identifiable features may vary, these other graphic variables are not manipulated directly in an image. They result from variation in the aspects of color across the image surface in combination with the resolution of the image. Uncertainty in an image, therefore, is confined to uncertainty about whether color used to depict locations (e.g., pixels) in that image matches their color in the environment. There can, of course, be considerable uncertainty about the interpretation of features identified from an image, but this uncertainty is a function of the viewer rather than of the representation and depends primarily on the viewer's experience and skill at image interpretation.

As we move along our continuum from images toward graphics, uncertainty (and the representation itself) begins to be more abstract. Uncertainty is no longer a matter of whether the image looks like the real thing at the specified place and time, but how well attributes of the display represent (in an abstract sense) attributes of the environment. Uncertainty in non-images, then, derives from variations in accuracy with which spatial, attribute, and temporal information is represented as well as mathematical and categorical precision with which that information is encoded. With a Landsat "image," for example, there is uncertainty in the accuracy of the signal received by the satellite due to atmospheric distortion and other factors and uncertainty due to the lack of precision (in terms of spatial resolution and color specification of the system used to display the scene on a monitor). Once classified, a Landsat scene has added uncertainty due to the categorical precision of the classification system used and to the necessary decision to assign each pixel to one of the available categories. For maps, uncertainty usually is greater (than for a digital satellite scene) due to variability in both accuracy of information (that may come from several sources) and variability in spatial precision (due to varying density of sample points or varying size of enumeration units to which data are aggregated). Attribute categories are also usually broader than for a classified Landsat scene and temporal precision is often less because a composite of information collected over a period of time is depicted and/or time may be aggregated (mean monthly CO concentration in the atmosphere).

At the graphic end of the image-graphic continuum, the kinds and amount of uncertainty will differ with the topic depicted. It can be confined to accuracy and mathematical precision of attribute specifications (e.g., a bar graph of PCB, lead, and mercury concentrations in a sample of fish taken from a polluted river) or may include all aspects of accuracy, mathematical precision, and categorical precision for space, time, and attributes (e.g., for a plot comparing changes over time in ozone concentrations for New York and Los Angeles).

## Representation Methods

Since the emphasis of this Primer is on maps and map design, attention here will be directed to representation methods for depicting uncertainty of mapped information. If uncertainty varies spatially (which it usually will for mapped information) a map of uncertainty will be much more useful than a verbal statement about uncertainty (particularly to an analyst using the map for exploratory or confirmatory visualization). As will be discussed in the next section, a choice must be made about whether or not to embed the data representation and uncertainty about that representation into the same map or to have separate maps of data and uncertainty. In either case we must rely on the same graphic language to represent uncertainty as we use to represent the environment. Similar arguments about the need to match kinds of variation in graphic variables to kinds of variation in uncertainty can be made. Quantitative specification of uncertainty should be depicted with graphic variables suited to showing order and qualitative distinctions should be depicted with those variables that imply differences in kind (e.g., point symbols of varying hue might be used to distinguish features that are questionable in terms of location, attributes, or time). We could also argue that for quantitative information, a logical choice of data model for the uncertainty information should be made (e.g., an uncertainty surface derived from probability estimates might be misleading if depicted with graduated circles, which would imply an abruptly varying discrete attribute of individual locations).

Beyond these basic guidelines, two graphic variables seem intuitively appealing for representing uncertainty: color saturation and focus. Both imply a lack of clarity or mixture of possibilities. Saturation is sometimes referred to as purity of a color. Highly saturated colors are intense with no doubt about their color hue. Unsaturated colors appear grayish due to the mixture of several hues. Therefore, uncertainty about the dominant hue will exist. Matching this visual uncertainty to uncertainty in some aspect of the representation should prove effective (although no empirical test of this idea has been conducted).[3] As an example, consider the isoline map of atmospheric particulates depicted in Figure 4.09A. This map is derived from samples taken by aircraft along the transects shown. Uncertainty in the isoline map produced, therefore, will vary with distance from these transects. A raster map of uncertainty can easily be calculated and could be represented by filling the cells with a single hue that varies in saturation in proportion to the uncertainty derived (Figure 4.09B).

Saturation might also be applied to depiction of uncertainty in existence (e.g., of illegal toxic waste sites). Figure 4.10 illustrates this application with symbol position indicating assumed location and saturation of the symbol indicating certainty about presence of a site.

Like saturation, focus seems intuitively logical as a way to depict uncertainty. Crispness of lines and symbols has long been a feature of accurate maps. Lack of crispness, therefore, should be immediately recognized (at least by experienced map readers) as an indication of some level of ambiguity. As a graphic variable, focus has

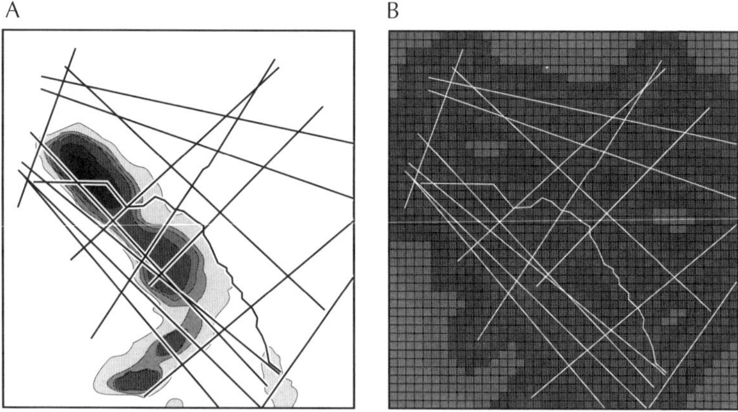


***Figure 4.09*** *Map pair depicting estimated atmospheric particulates and certainty about those estimates. Source for map A: EPA 1991. See color version Figure C4.09.*

been given even less attention than saturation. It has been suggested, however, that there are at least four ways in which symbol focus can be manipulated (MacEachren, 1992). These are:

1) Edge crispness—As indicated in Chapter 2, one interpretation of the concept of focus is to vary the crispness of symbol edges. This kind of change in focus should provide an obvious indication of spatial uncertainty. Focus could, for example, be used similarly to saturation in the map of toxic waste sites. In this case edge crispness depicts uncertainty in location of the sites (Figure 4.11). Edges of areas, as well as points, can be defocused as shown in Figure 2.03. A similar application of this aspect of focus to boundary lines has been proposed by van der Wel (1993).

2) Fill clarity—While edge crispness intuitively suggests uncertainty in position, the crispness of elements making up interior fills can be logically associated with attribute uncertainty. Sharp, distinct patterns might indicate certain attribute categorization for an area while fuzzy patterns imply uncertainty (Figure 4.12, page 82).

3) Fog—On some display devices, it is possible to use translucent patterns of fine texture that give the impression of looking through a fog or atmospheric haze. Rather than changing the focus of individual symbols, therefore, such a fog could be used to alter the focus or clarity of various sections of a map display. Analysts would see varying thicknesses of fog between themselves and the map as varying amounts of uncertainty across the map (Figure 4.13, page 82).

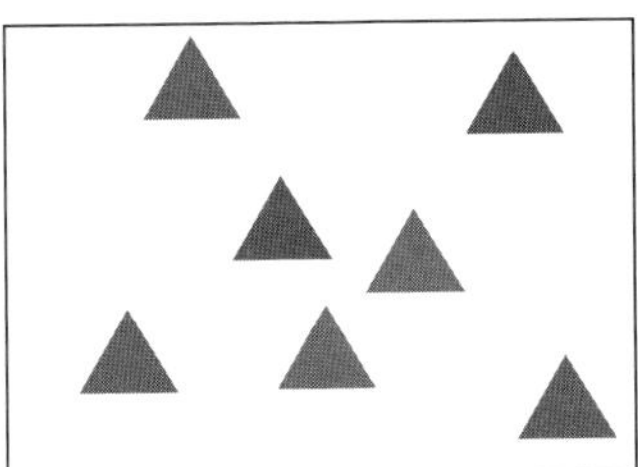

***Figure 4.10*** *Uncertainty in the existence of toxic waste dumps depicted by changes in saturation. See color version, Figure C4.10.*

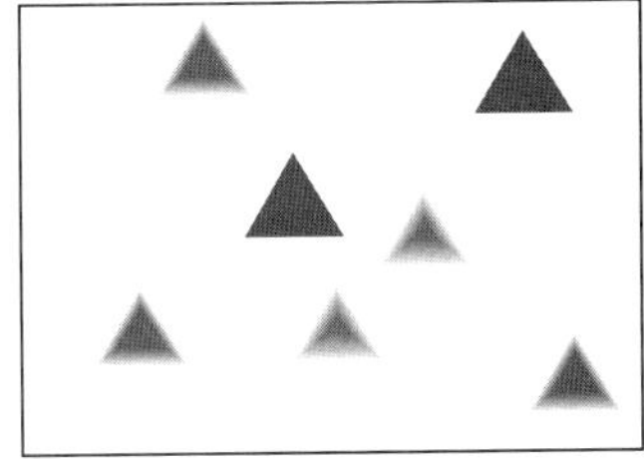

***Figure 4.11*** *Uncertainty in the location of toxic waste dumps depicted by changes in focus.*

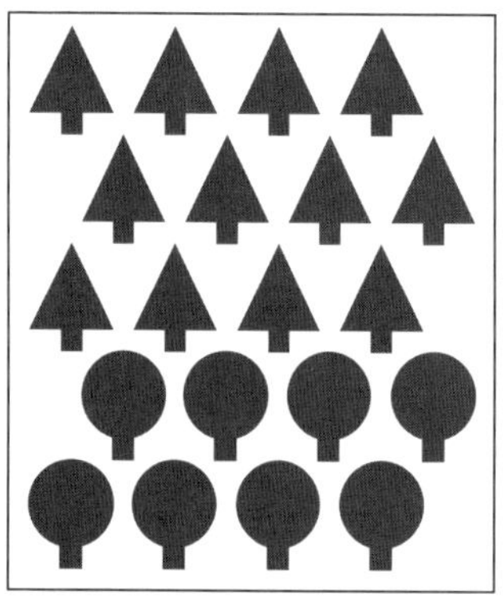

*Figure 4.12 A certain (left) and an uncertain (right) classification as coniferous versus deciduous forest.*

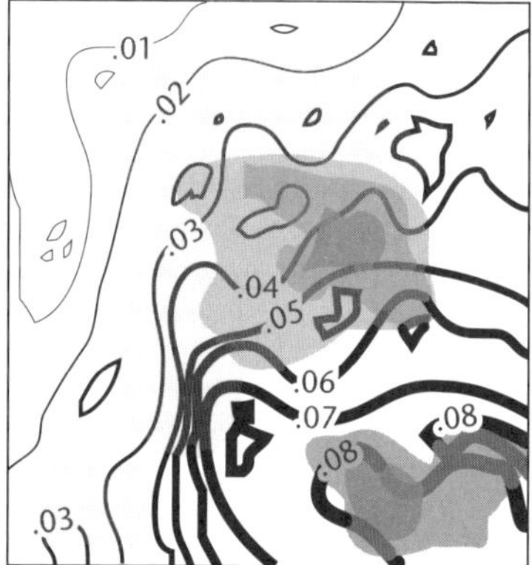


*Figure 4.13 Map of the ecological risk due to ozone. On the left, isolines depict a composite risk index and on the right, the uncertainty in that index is overlayed as a "fog" of varying thickness corresponding to varying degrees of uncertainty. Reproduced from MacEachren (1992) with permission.*

4) An alternative way to conceptualize the focus variable is to treat it as a variation in resolution. On a computer monitor, then, focus could be adjusted through image enhancement or degradation techniques developed for remote sensing. Also, a map base might be "de-focused" to indicate the resolution (and the uncertainty) inherent in model produced data (Figure 4.14).

In addition to deciding how uncertainty should be represented, a decision must be made concerning how these representations will

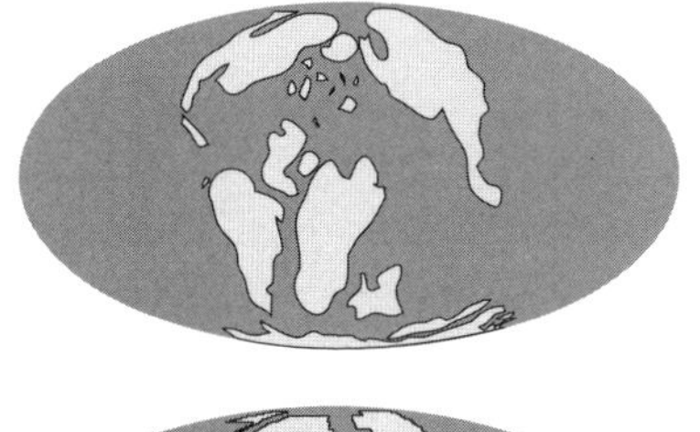

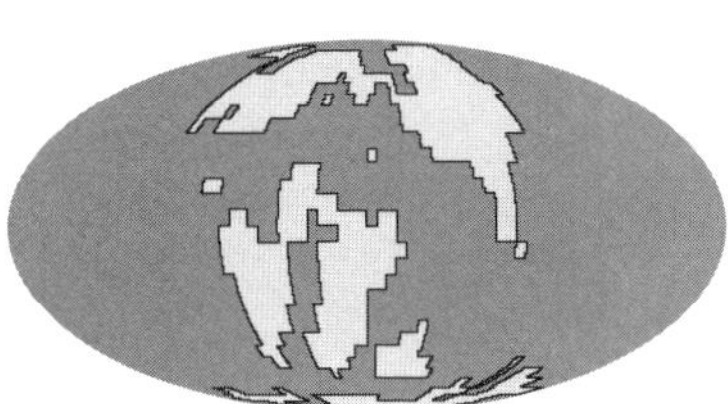

*Figure 4.14* In this pair of maps, the hypothesized position of the continents in the Eocene is shown, together with a generalized "de-focused" depiction that emphasizes the resolution of global climate models that are used to speculate on what past climates were like. (After DiBiase, et al. 1991.)

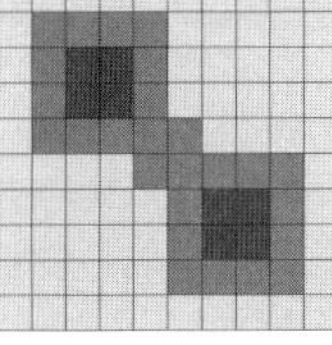

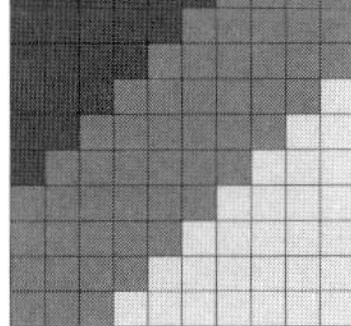

*Figure 4.15* Schematic illustration of a data-uncertainty map pair. Reproduced from MacEachren (1992) with permission.

be presented. The best method for presenting uncertainty information will depend on the map applications and the environment in which the maps are displayed. Cartographic presentations can take at least three forms. The most obvious is to show the viewer side-by-side maps of the topic and uncertainty about the topic, as demonstrated in Figure 4.15, and in Figure 4.09. Most cartographic attempts to deal with representing accuracy, data quality, or uncertainty to date have fit in this category.

An alternative to side-by-side map pairs that becomes available in an interactive GIS environment is sequential presentation of topical and uncertainty information (Figure 4.16, page 84). Such presentation will probably be most effective if an analyst is allowed to toggle back and forth between the two views making use of visual memory to mentally superimpose them. The advantage of this procedure over side-by-side viewing is the significant increase in map scale that is possible when only one rather than two maps are displayed on a monitor.

Perhaps the most interesting possibility, but one that requires further evaluation, is to embed topical information and uncertainty in the same map. The maps of toxic waste dump locations using

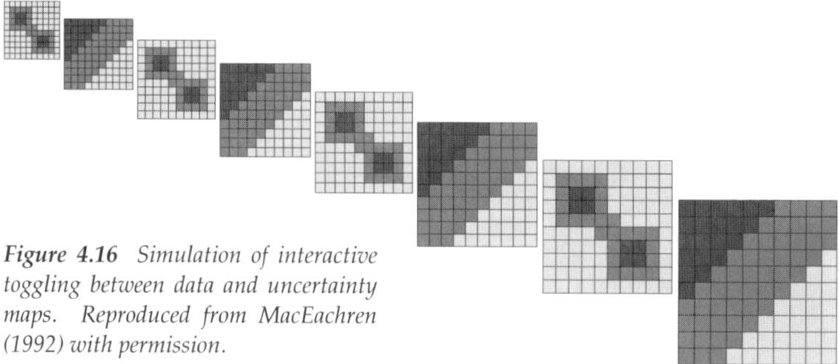

*Figure 4.16* Simulation of interactive toggling between data and uncertainty maps. Reproduced from MacEachren (1992) with permission.

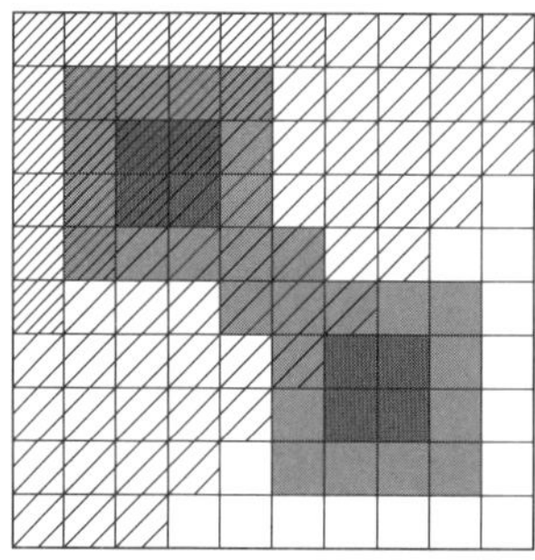

*Figure 4.17* A bivariate data-uncertainty map. Reproduced from MacEachren (1992) with permission.

saturation and focus presented above provide simple examples of this possibility. When the topical variable is quantitative, we might generate bivariate maps that depict the data and metadata in a single view (Figure 4.17). Bivariate choropleth maps have not proved to be particularly effective when depicting relationships between two distinct variables (e.g., Olson, 1981). A bivariate map in which an ordered hue sequence depicts topical information and a range in saturation of those hues depicts uncertainty, however, may prove more successful because the relationships should be more easily understood. For black and white maps, a value-texture combination may be effective.

## Summary

The quality of interpretations made using cartographic visualization tools will depend upon the abstraction decisions made in creating displays and user understanding of them. Although human vision is a powerful pattern identification system, it can be fooled. We must, therefore, guard against being fooled into seeing wrong or not seeing. One method of achieving this goal is to use the flexibility of GIS to view data from multiple perspectives so that we can assess pattern stability. In addition, we must give more attention to uncertainty in the information depicted by GIS (on maps or in other forms). With a GIS, uncertainty may be multiplied (rather than simply added) due to processes by which different layers of information are combined. Tools for directly representing uncertainty in position, time, and attributes are required. The graphic variables of saturation and focus seem well suited to such representation.

## Endnotes

[1]*Monmonier (1991b) has gone so far as to suggest that providing a single view is unethical.*

[2]*The ideas presented here were stimulated by an invitation to participate in the National Center for Geographic Information and Analysis Specialist's Meeting on Visualization of Data Quality, Initiative 7 (Beard and Buttenfield 1991). I gratefully acknowledge the invitation and travel support provided by the NCGIA through their National Science Foundation Grant # SES-88-10917. The perspective presented began as a "working paper" for that event, "Visualization of Data Uncertainty: Representational Issues," which was circulated only to the 25 participants of the meeting and within the NCGIA. A revision and expansion of that working paper subsequently appeared in MacEachren (1992). Several other papers from the same meeting have been expanded and organized into a special issue of Cartographica. Interested readers are encouraged to consult that issue (Buttenfield in press).*

[3]*Brown and van Elzakker (1993) have, however, conducted a detailed analysis of the technological issues of using hue/saturation combinations on maps of qualitative data and certainty about that data. They recommend no more than three quality categories using saturation.*

# 5

# COMPOSING THE DISPLAY

*Combining ideas about the role of maps in geographic analysis and presentation, cartographic language, map abstraction, and visualization quality, we are equipped to address some design issues involved in composing the map display. Whether for interactive analysis on a computer monitor or final presentation on a printed page, composition requires a large number of interlinked decisions. This final chapter begins by addressing several decisions that together establish the maps's visual and conceptual logic: creation of a graphic hierarchy, the use of color hue, value, and saturation to deal with the complexity of multivariate mapping problems, establishing an appropriate geographic context, and construction of informative map legends. Some guidelines on how to adapt to various design and symbolization constraints imposed by different display media are then presented.*

## Visual and Conceptual Organization

### Graphic Hierarchy

Among the most important organization issues is how to direct viewer attention toward or away from aspects of the available information — the creation of a graphic hierarchy. At the exploratory end of analysis, the analyst should be able to control the graphic hierarchy by manipulating various graphic variables in an effort to isolate patterns or important elements of a particular pattern. As investigation moves from initial exploration toward final presentation of a scientific analysis or a policy decision, the goal changes from identifying patterns and relationships to emphasizing a particular pattern or relationship or persuading an audience of a particular policy. In this case, a graphic hierarchy can be designed that draws attention to the pertinent information.

Establishing (or interactively manipulating) the map's graphic hierarchy involves a concept termed figure-ground, the visual separation of a scene into recognizable figures and inconspicuous background. A variety of methods exist for ensuring that a particular feature will stand out as figure. These methods make use of contrast in graphic variables along with map layout decisions designed to draw attention to particular features. One general principle to follow is that value contrasts work well to separate points or lines from areas or one area from another. Guidelines in some texts suggest that dark areas will be figure if all other things are held equal. This guideline has been demonstrated to be incorrect (MacEachren and Mistrick 1992). In general the smaller of two areas that contrast in value will usually stand out as figure (Figure 5.01) but value contrast alone for areas of equal size will create ambiguity. In these cases, texture contrast is effective in removing the ambiguity, with coarser textures usually standing out as figure (Figure 5.02). Like color value, orientation differences produce contrast, but are ambiguous in terms of figure-ground unless one area is smaller than another. In this case, the smaller of two areas with differently oriented fills appears as figure (Figure 5.03).

If color hue is available, contrasting hues that also contrast in value (e.g., yellow-black, white-blue) produce the best figure-ground relationships, with smaller areas, again, usually seen as figure. In addition, there is a slight tendency for long wavelength hues to stand out. Red therefore, makes a better figure color than blue. Use of complementary colors (e.g., red-green, blue-orange) does not work well because complements are hard to discriminate.

***Figure 5.01*** *Value contrast is used here to visually differentiate two map regions (a chemical spill and a section of open sea). The difference in size between the chemical spill and the surrounding sea causes the spill area to appear as figure regardless of whether the shading is black spill-white sea or the reverse. Black oil is of course, the more mimetic choice.*

In addition to manipulating contrast in one or more graphic variables, figures can be enhanced by creating a strong, crisp edge between the figure and background (Figure 5.04), by adjusting geographic scope so that the figure is centrally located and closed (Figure 5.05, page 90), and by creating an appearance that the figure is interposed between the viewer and the background (Figure 5.06, page 90). These latter methods are well suited to emphasizing one geographic region of a map as figure in relation to its surroundings or to drawing attention to a legend so it will be studied before the reader attempts to read the map (Figure 5.07, page 90).

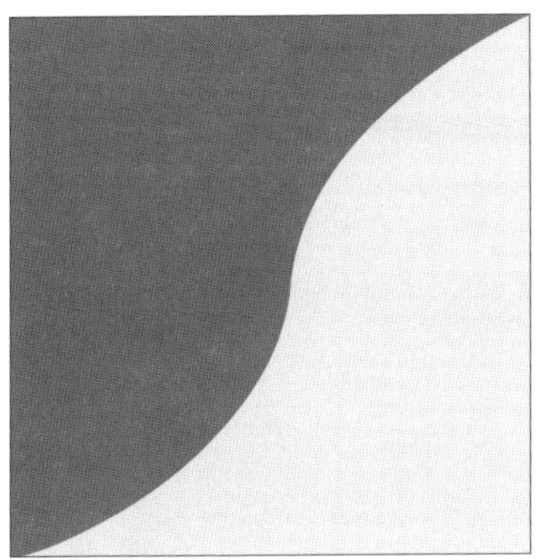

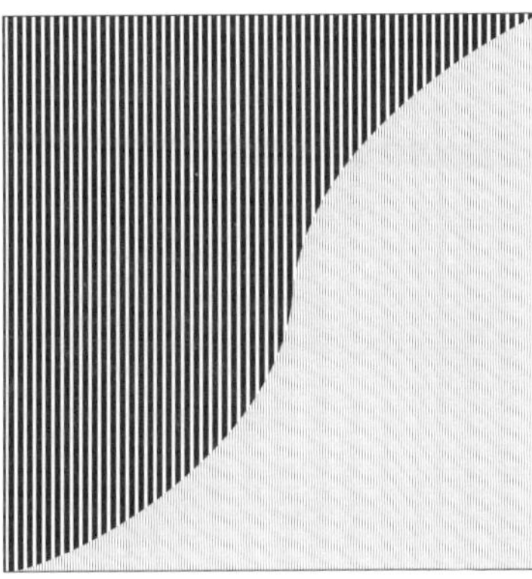

**Figure 5.02** *Ambiguous figure-ground relationships can be clarified by a change in texture with coarse textures usually appearing as figure.*

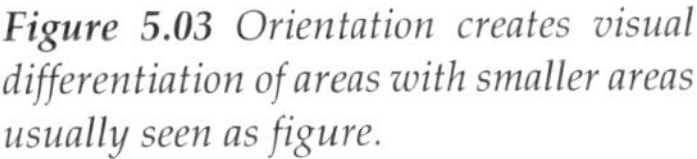

**Figure 5.03** *Orientation creates visual differentiation of areas with smaller areas usually seen as figure.*

**Figure 5.04** *Strong edges (called "good contour" by Gestalt psychologists) enhance the appearance of figure.*

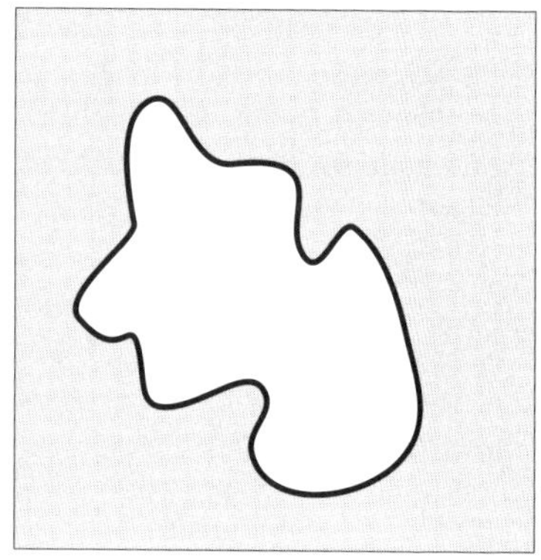

*Figure 5.05* Centrally located features are more easily seen as figure.

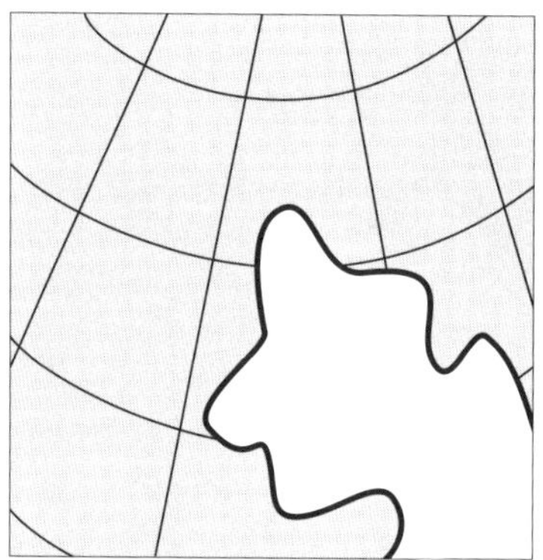

*Figure 5.06* An area that appears to hide part of the background will appear to be floating in front or on top of that background and will, therefore, be seen as a strong figure.

*Figure 5.07* Superimposition can draw attention to legend information as well as to map features.

In a dynamic environment (e.g., an animated map on videotape), movement across space will create a strong sensation of figure. Things that move together will also appear grouped together or associated in some way. They will become one figure. It is likely that the human tendency to focus on motion will be mimicked in a tendency to focus on change in stationary attributes as well. If so, changing features can be expected to stand out as figure in relation to static features.

**Color Logic for Multivariate Maps**

Not all color maps are as simple as the examples used in Chapter 2 or the one described in the preceding section. Computers have increased the availability of color for maps, but this increased availability brings with it the need to develop logical strategies for color use. Color has particular potential for increasing the effectiveness of multivariate representations, but only if it is matched logically to data characteristics. In this section, guidelines are provided for integrating the cartographic language principles identified in Chapter 2 (for use of color hue, value, and saturation) in order to facilitate multivariate representation.[1]

At a simple level, consider depicting a set of numerical information that spans some critical value (e.g., zero, a national average, etc.) as bidirectional (or diverging from this critical value), rather than unidirectional (ordered sequentially from low to high). By putting emphasis on the diverging nature of the data, we have created what is in essence a multivariate representation problem. Whether a value is above or below the break point can be treated as a qualitative distinction and distance from that break point in each direction can be treated as two numerical variables. With this conceptualization of the situation, a hue difference makes sense as a way to distinguish the two ends of the scale and a value difference within each hue can be used to depict the numerical ranges. The cancer incidence data of Figure 2.22 is a case in point. A primary goal of the map is to highlight those counties in Pennsylvania that are either worse or better off than the national average. As an alternative to using texture for the qualitative distinction (as done in Figure 2.22) we can substitute a hue difference (red for above the mean and blue below). The result is a map that is easier to interpret, and less visually harsh (Figure 5.08, page 92).

A similar kind of multivariate problem occurs when two sets of balanced proportions are to be mapped. In this case, the goal is to represent the balance between two portions of a whole, both of which could be depicted independently (e.g., % male vs. % female; % with a high school education vs. % without a high school education ; % white vs. % persons of color, etc.). As Brewer (in press) points out, this kind of 'balance' problem is a special case of the more general problem of depicting two univariate data sets on a single bivariate map. When mapping the balance of two univariate

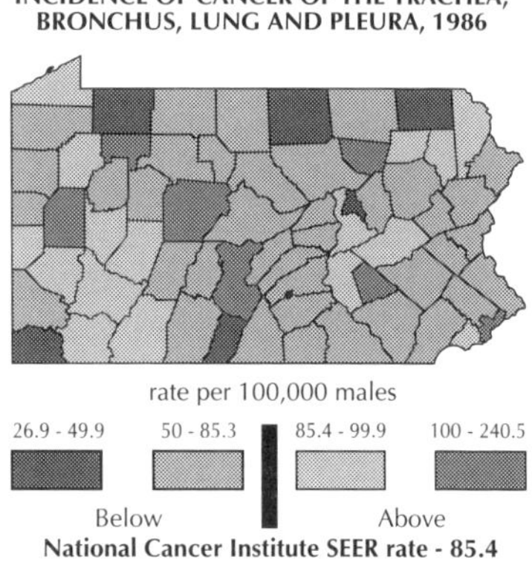


***Figure 5.08*** *The cancer incidence map from Figure 2.22 reproduced with texture replaced by color hue. On this map, the data are treated as bidirectional rather than unidirectional (as they were in Figure 2.22). As a result, the counties with particularly low and particularly high rates are emphasized. See color version, Figure C5.08.*

data sets, the middle of the range (highly balanced populations) is likely to be as interesting to the map user as the extremes. When this is the case, it is important to select a color scheme that does not emphasize the extremes over the midpoint (or the reverse) and one in which colors of the middle categories logically connote mixing. Using a scheme that gives the appearance of mixture in the middle categories is ideal, and if the midpoint is to be emphasized the scheme should produce a middle hue that is at least somewhat distinctive.

An intriguing attempt at such a color scheme is the one used by authors of *The State of the Nation*, an atlas of the United Kingdom (Fothergill and Vincent 1985). In their map of Protestant and Catholic population of Northern Ireland, the authors used a seven-category color scheme ranging from green at one end through yellow-greens, yellow, and yellow-oranges to orange at the other end. This scheme creates a double ended scale with yellow (a high value or light color) at the midpoint and lower value colors of green and orange at either extreme (Figure 5.09). The yellow midpoint is relatively distinct. Green for Catholic and orange for Protestant match the color connotations associated with the two groups in the area. That yellow is not a mixed hue may connote a lack of mixing in these areas of combined population. An alternative to this color scheme that enhances the sensation of mixing for the middle categories (while deemphasizing the midpoint) is a range from red through purple to blue. These colors (in contrast to the green, yellow, orange sequence) have little value difference if used at full saturation. To be effective, some lightening of the middle purples is required.

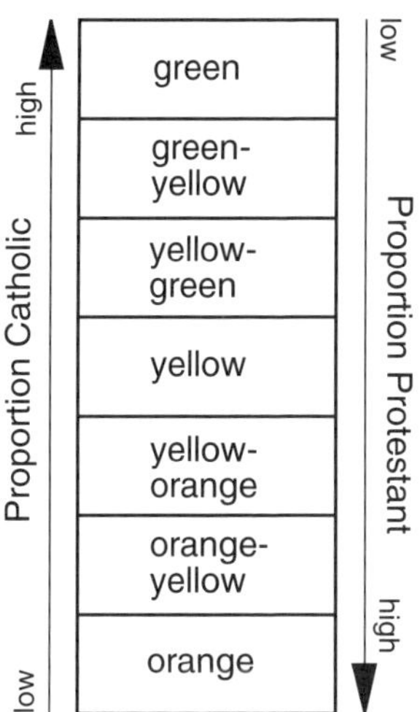


***Figure 5.09*** *The legend structure for the Northern Ireland map. Category assignments for the map use a divergent range centered on yellow. Yellow areas on the map depict districts that have a nearly equal mix of Catholics and Protestants. Orange and green represent segregated districts in which only Protestants or only Catholics reside. After Fothergill and Vincent (1985, plate 24, p.57).*

Both multivariate color application problems discussed thus far deal with enumerated data collected for a constant set of units. This situation is common in the spatial analysis of socioeconomic data. In many applications of GIS for planning or environmental analysis, however, a second kind of multivariate problem arises, the representation of map overlay and/or variable conjunctions. Brewer (1993) provides several examples of color assignments that should and should not be used for GIS style map overlay (for both qualitative-quantitative and quantitative-quantitative combinations). Among the examples she provides is a map combining soil drainage and distance to surface water. Such a map would be typical of the visualization tools an analyst might use in trying to identify potential sites for a campground in a national forest. A similar problem to which Brewer's color guidelines can be applied is the location of soils suitable for use as 'cut-off' material for leaking sanitary landfills. A study by McLay (1987) has demonstrated the advantages of bivariate color maps over standard soils maps for this purpose. The main requirement for cut-off materials is that soils be impermeable (poorly drained). Soil that is impermeable, however, typically has a high clay content. Clay soils tend to be very hard when dry and very sticky when wet, characteristics that make them unsuitable (from a construction perspective) for acquisition and transport to a landfill site.

The goal of map analysis for the landfill problem identified is to locate impermeable soils that are not high in clay. An additional practical requirement is that a sufficient contiguous area of acceptable soils exist for "mining" the soil to be economical. For the real world problem that served as a model in the example presented here, the minimum area was set at approximately ten acres (about the size of the legends for maps used in Figure 5.10). A bivariate map representing permeability and percent clay (given a suitable color assignment) can be quite effective in identifying such soils. One choice for color assignment, frequently found on bivariate maps, is a full-spectral sequence in which the colors of the spectrum are wrapped around the perimeter of a 3 X 3 legend with a neutral (e.g., brown) in the center (Figure 5.10-top). As the example demonstrates, the categories are discriminable but the viewer must work quite hard to identify areas that have a combination of generally low permeability and acceptably low clay content (i.e., the three legend categories in the lower left). A more successful map can be achieved by applying the logic that each quantitative variable should be depicted with a color value range and the appropriate versus inappropriate sites should be qualitatively differentiated. One scheme that Brewer demonstrates does just this. The scheme employs a value range of the complementary colors yellow and blue to depict the two variables (saturated to unsaturated yellow for high to low permeability and saturated to unsaturated blue for low to high clay content) (Figure 5.10-bottom). On this map, any yellowish cell depicts a possible location for soil used in the cut-off, any blue represents a poor location, and any neutral gray represents a location of intermediate potential. The yellow-blue scheme is ideal if the soil permeability and clay content variables are treated as equally important. If, however, soil permeability was given a higher priority, another of Brewer's schemes (a value-lightness scheme) would be more effective. With light to dark red representing soil of low to high permeability and fully saturated to unsaturated representing high to low clay content, any dark map area would be off limits as a source for cut-off soil, while light regions would be possible (with the less saturated of those being preferred).

## Geographic Context

While choices about map symbolization will establish the map's overall visual and conceptual logic, selection of map scale and of the map's center will control the geographic context within which an analysis takes place, as well as the detail at which that analysis

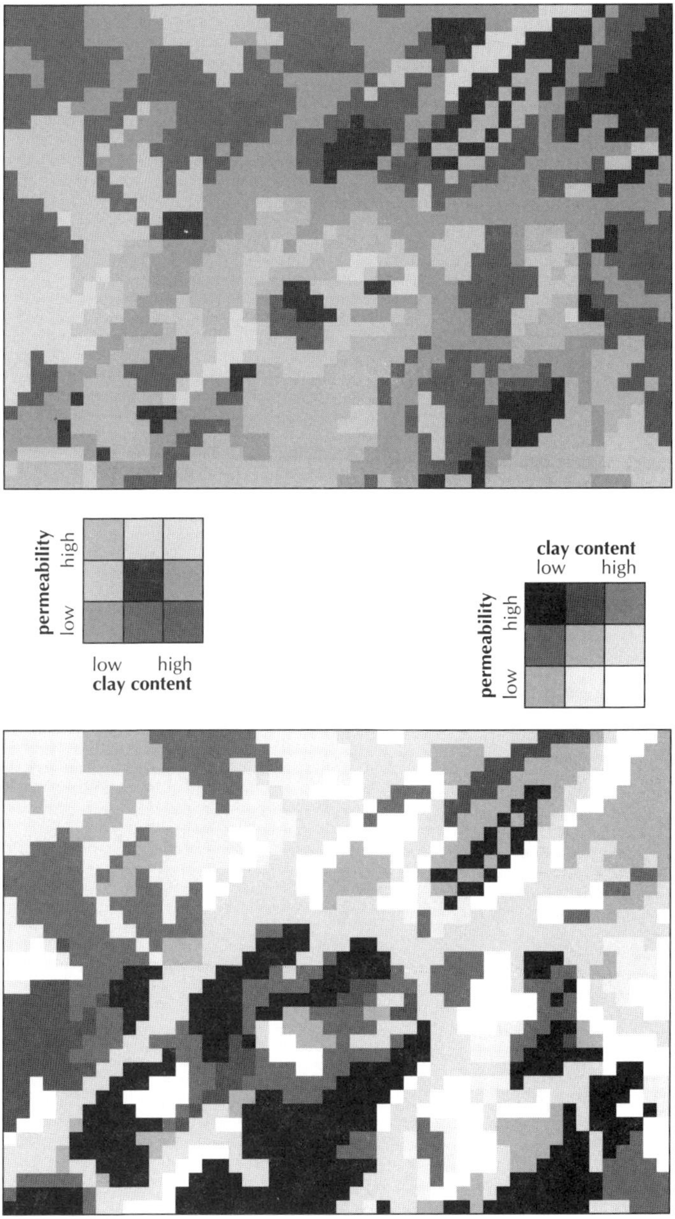

***Figure 5.10*** *Soil permeability overlaid with clay content to produce a bivariate map. The top color scheme is full-spectral. The bottom map uses the same data as above, but with complementary colors depicting the two variables. Color schemes depicted are modeled on Brewer (1993) and applied to a problem illustrated in McLay (1987).*

can be made. As Monmonier and Johnson (1990) point out, choice of scale is also likely to influence a presentation map viewer's attitude concerning the relative importance of an environmental problem. If a relatively small map scale is chosen, the geographic region of focus will be a clear figure and its relative position in relation to a broader geographic context will be apparent, but the environmental problem depicted may appear insignificant because it seems to affect only a small portion of the map (Figure 5.11). Zooming in on a problem region, on the other hand, might cause some viewers to panic because the problem appears to be everywhere (Figure 5.12).

One solution to this potential for misunderstanding or confusion about geographic context is to combine a close-up with a locational inset map. For example, some readers of this Primer will not know exactly where Commencement Bay is located and may, therefore, not realize the significance of the contamination for the large surrounding population or even for the immediately adjacent areas. A regional locator and/or a state locator map will eliminate this problem (Figure 5.13). As a general guideline, it can be assumed that the smaller the region or the more distant it is from the viewer's home, the less familiar it will be, therefore, the more need there will be for a locational inset.

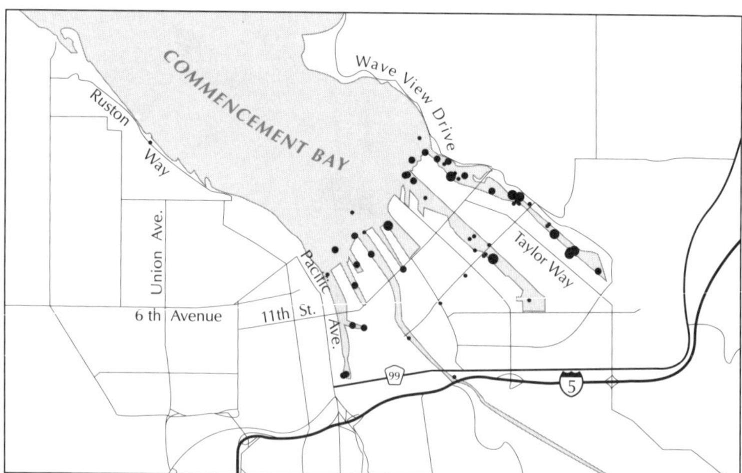


***Figure 5.11*** *A misleading depiction of hazardous chemical concentrations in Commencement Bay which suggests that the problem is a localized one and, as a result, that it is not very significant. Source: EPA (1991).*

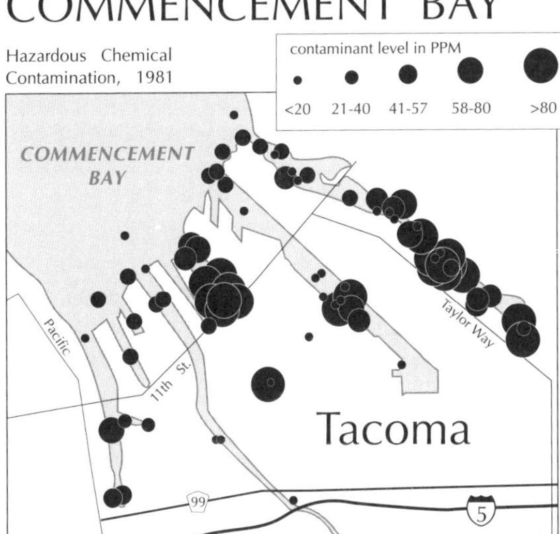


*Figure 5.12* *Zooming in on a problem changes the impression to one of a major problem with few areas uncontaminated. This view will appear much more alarming than that of Figure 5.11. Source: EPA (1991).*

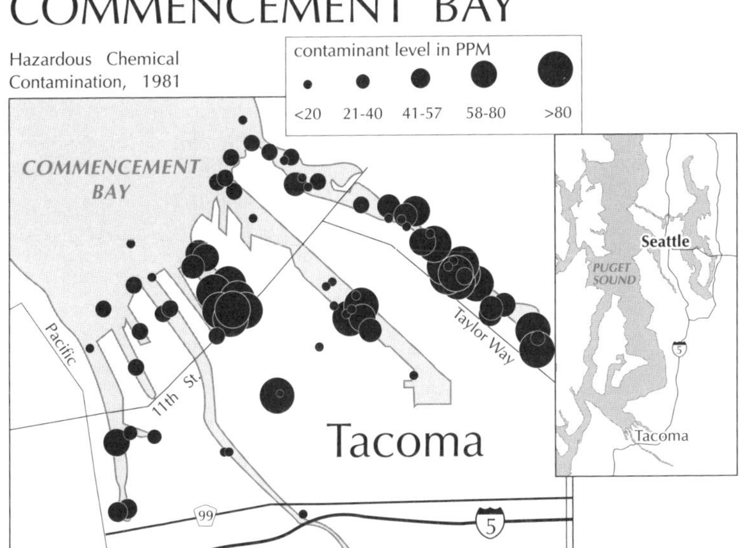


*Figure 5.13* *This map depicts the site's location in relation to Seattle and to Puget Sound. Source: EPA (1991).*

## Marginal Information

A final aspect of visual and conceptual organization to be considered here is the information that appears in the map's margin. This information is particularly vital for presentation maps, but indications of scale, delineation of geographic orientation, and legend specifications will also be relevant when dynamic exploratory analysis allows these factors to change rapidly.

On presentation maps, labels and titles should be selected carefully to help establish the geographic, topical, and temporal context. It is best to use a concise title that provides the essential details of place, time, and general topic (e.g., hazardous chemicals in Commencement Bay, Washington, 1981) with further details provided in a legend heading (e.g., contaminant levels of bottom sediment in ppm). Obvious legend headings (e.g., "key" or "legend") should be avoided because they add no information and take up valuable space.[2]

Adequate source information should also be included on all presentation maps (or in a caption, appendix, etc. if the map is part of a report). For any topic in which data collection occurs over an extended period and/or the date of map production differs substantially from the date of data collection, these temporal details should be addressed in a note (within the map borders of a sheet map or in a caption or appendix of a report map). Care should be taken when specifying a date for data, to take into account differences between the date data were collected and the date that the data became available (e.g., much of the demographic data provided by the Census Bureau is not published until about two years after collection).

Much has been said in cartographic texts about the need for directional indicators and scales on all maps. For exploratory maps, however, these spatial referencing aids are required only if scale or orientation changes as part of dynamic analysis procedures. If both scale and orientation of the map are static, a knowledgeable analyst would seldom need to have this information explicitly portrayed. Even for presentation maps, particularly small maps of large areas, an indication of scale can be omitted from maps of a well known place for which distance measurements are unlikely to be attempted (e.g., a page-sized map of the U.S. showing environmental risk zones does not require a scale because viewers know roughly how big the U.S. is and they will not be measuring distances across a map at this scale).

Similarly, directional indicators are needed on presentation maps only when directions are not obvious. The map of risk to water sources in Pennsylvania (see Figure 3.01, middle), for example, is quite usable even though latitude and longitude are not indicated. A common mistake in presentation maps is to fulfill the cartographic guideline that all maps should have directional indicators by adding a north arrow to a map in which this style of directional indication is misleading. For example, the Goode's projection typical for distribution maps of the world (Figure 4.02) has curved meridians that converge toward the poles, both of which are depicted as having multiple locations. Although it is possible to indicate north with an arrow anywhere on the map, that indication is only accurate along one meridian and is misleading concerning orientations on the remainder of the map. Again the best guide to follow is that directional indicators should be included whenever an unusual orientation is used (i.e., east up), when directions are not obvious (e.g., because they are changing dynamically), or when precise geographic location of points on the map are important to understanding the topic mapped or using the map information. North arrows should only appear on relatively large scale maps for which they are applicable everywhere. A geographic grid (parallels and meridians) should be used whenever the map is at a small scale (particularly when the graticule of the projection is curved and when precise positions are relevant).

A final issue to be addressed concerning the map's marginal information is the design of legends. Legend information should be organized logically with key items of the map display highlighted (Figure 5.14, page 100). On maps in which ordered sequences of area fills are used to depict ordered data, the legend can be designed to indicate non-contiguous or contiguous categories (Figure 5.15, page 100). Data range and frequency within each legend category can also be indicated by creating a legend in the form of a graph. This provides some additional information about the topic depicted without taking up significantly more space (Figure 5.16, page 100).

For presentation maps, particularly those using isolines (a rela-

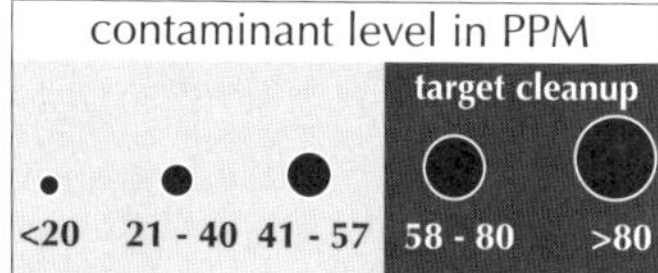


*Figure 5.14* *A legend to accompany the map of contaminants in Commencement Bay for which the target cleanup goal has been highlighted. Source: EPA (1991).*

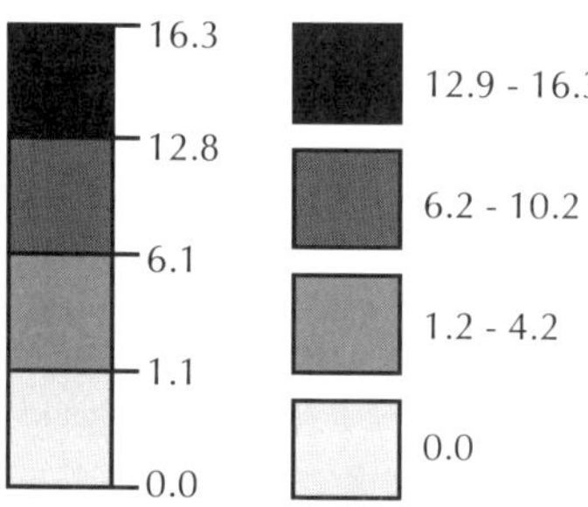


*Figure 5.15* *Legends designed to indicate contiguous versus discrete categories.*

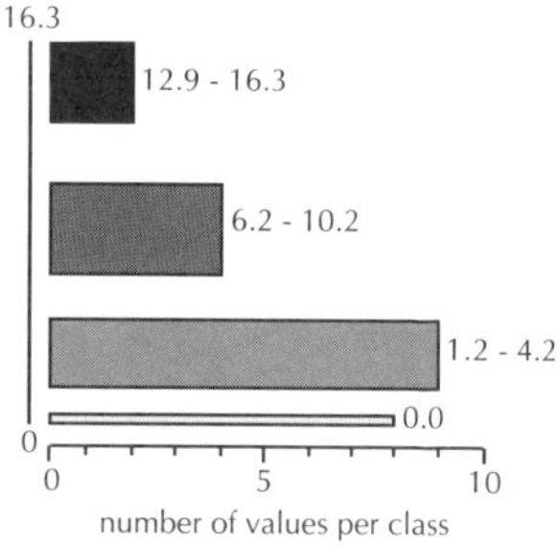

16.3
12.9 - 16.3
6.2 - 10.2
1.2 - 4.2
0.0
0
0
5
10
number of values per class

*Figure 5.16* *A legend designed to communicate the relative range of categories and frequency of values within each category.*

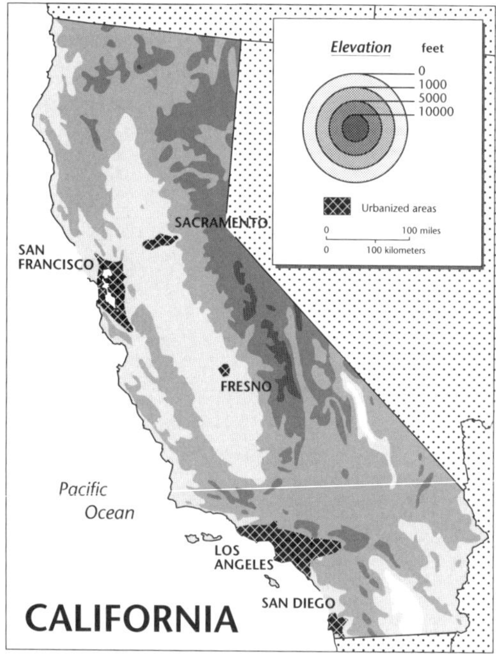


*Figure 5.17* *A schematic natural legend may help viewers visualize the continuous three-dimensional surface implied by relatively abstract two-dimensional patterns of isometric lines.*

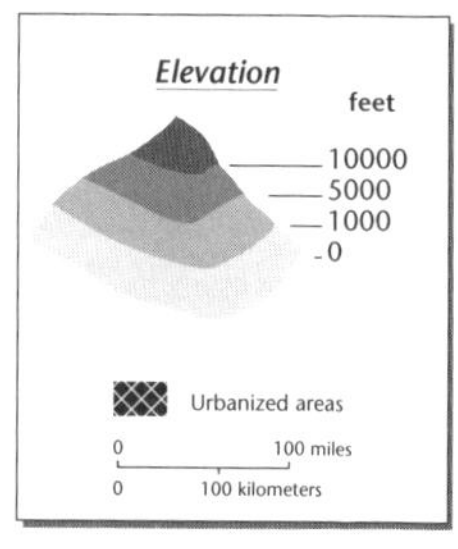


*Figure 5.18* *A more realistic natural legend can be created easily by most GIS packages that are capable of producing the 2D isometric map.*

tively abstract symbol), DeLucia and Hiller (1982) advocate use of natural legends—legends that are similar in appearance to the map symbolization (Figure 5.17). They demonstrated that non-expert map readers were better able to grasp the idea of a continuous surface from an isoline depiction with this style of legend. With most GIS, creating a 3D natural legend should be a simple matter (Figure 5.18). A 3D legend on a 2D isometric map combines the advantages of a 3D depiction to prompt a mental visualization of the overall shape of the surface depicted with the advantages of a 2D (plan view) map to provide a base (with no hidden surfaces) for plotting other information.

## Matching the Map to the Media

### Reports—Black and White

Probably the most obvious constraint imposed on analytical maps comes about when the distribution medium for a synthesis or presentation map is a black and white report. In this case, we lose two entire graphic variables, color hue and color saturation. This is particularly problematic because most computer workstations have color monitors, so our visual thinking graphics (i.e., those used in exploration and confirmation) are in full color. If these displays are printed without adjustment, both hue and saturation differences will be changed to value differences, often with disastrous results. In general, the change from screen display to black and white map will demand a redesign substituting alternative graphic variables for hue and saturation. For example, the saturation range used in Figure 4.12 to depict uncertainty might be replaced with a texture range (Figure 5.19, page 102) or a distinction between public water wells and water quality test points that had been made with blue versus red filled circles could be changed to different shaped black symbols (Figure 5.20, page 102).

One advantage of black and white report maps is that they can be produced at a higher resolution than most display screens are capable of (300 dpi versus about 60 dpi on a standard high resolution color monitor).[3] This added resolution means that text and symbols can be smaller, differences in symbol shapes, sizes, etc. can be less, and the overall detail can be greater than is possible on the screen. On a black and white printed page, lettering as small as about 5 points is legible (although just barely for some people), type

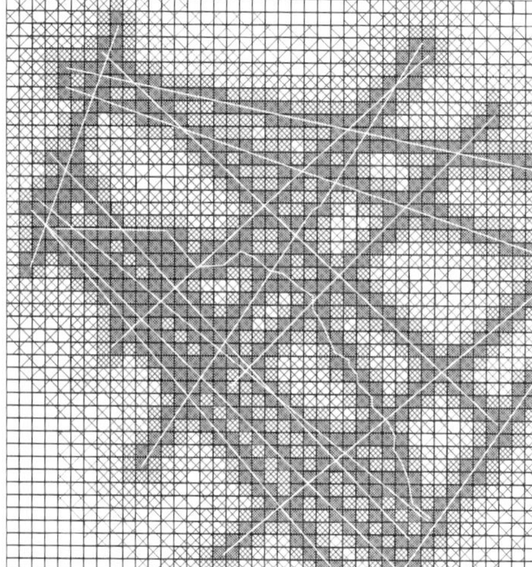

*Figure 5.19* Redesign of Figure 4.09 for reproduction in black and white. Increasing certainty in atmospheric particulates is now shown by increasingly fine texture.

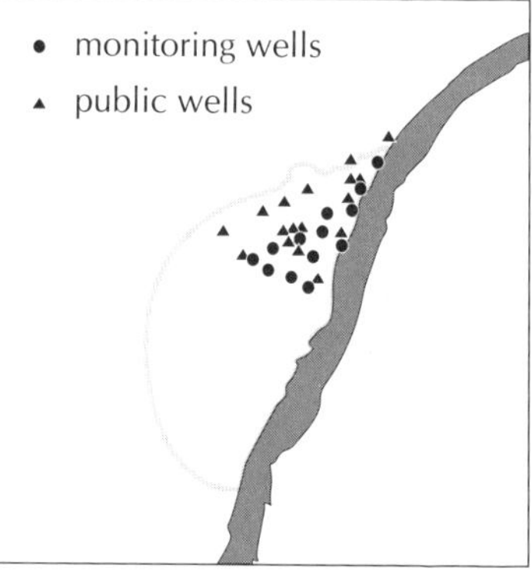


*Figure 5.20* A map depicting locations of water supply and monitoring wells for a section of St. Charles County Missouri along with results of a model indicating the probable 10 year well field (the light gray line). Map derived from a full color sheet map produced as part of a cooperative study involving OGWP, EMSL-LV, and Missouri DNR. Source: EPA (1991).

size differences of about 35% are recognizable, line widths down to 0.5 points (approximately 0.03 in.) can be used with differences of about 50% noticeable (Keates, 1982), and 5 to 7 color values (created with dot or line patterns) will be easily distinguished (with more value steps discriminable when fills have coarser textures).

One issue that cartographic research of the past three decades has looked at quite closely is the selection of an ordered sequence of color values that are intended to imply a similar sequence of data values. It is clear that people can only distinguish a limited number color values (i.e., gray tones on a black and white map) and values look different when adjacent to different darkness. This makes using color value problematic if our goal is to depict many data values. We have two options. Data can be grouped into 7 or fewer categories (as discussed in Chapter 3) which can then be treated as ordinal information, or we can apply a one-to-one mapping of data values to color values (an n-class map) and accept the fact that comparison of data values for specific places will suffer at the expense of a truer overall impression of spatial variability.

The first option (classed maps) is most appropriate for synthesis and presentation applications designed to emphasize major categorical differences in the phenomenon depicted. In this case, color values are selected that are as discriminable as possible so that there is little chance for a viewer to confuse the order. Selecting the set of color values that are most discriminable is not as straightforward as it might at first seem. For most monochrome cartographic applications gray tones are created by filling areas with small repeated lines or dots that cover a specified percentage of the page with ink. This process is also required to make multicolor map printing possible at reasonable expense, but is not required on color computer displays which can generate specified hue, value, and saturation levels directly as solid fills.

When fills are produced by line or dot patterns, apparent values will vary with the texture of the area fill that is used (Kimerling 1985). For fine-textured patterns (e.g., those produced on a Linotronic or other phototypesetting machine), most people have more trouble distinguishing between dark color values than between light color values. To achieve the most discriminable set of area fills in this case requires a non-linear spacing of actual color values. For a black and white six-class map with 120 lpi area fills, Kimerling (1985) determined that a subset of the well known Munsell gray-scale (covering the reflectance range of typical cartographic paper and inks) was appropriate (Figure 5.21, page 104). This gray-scale, when converted to more convenient percent-area-inked terms, indicates that 120 lpi patterns of 0%, 10%, 26%, 45%, 68%, and 100% area filled will be equally discriminable on a high resolution printed map (Figure 5.22, page 104). For coarser area fills (42 lpi) of the kind produced on a laser printer, however, Leonard and Buttenfield (1989) found an S-shaped relationship between measured reflectance and perceived value that resulted in a need for larger differences in the middle and light end of the range than at the dark end (Figure 5.23, page 104).[4] Translating from display to laser printer generated reports, therefore, will cause a map that has

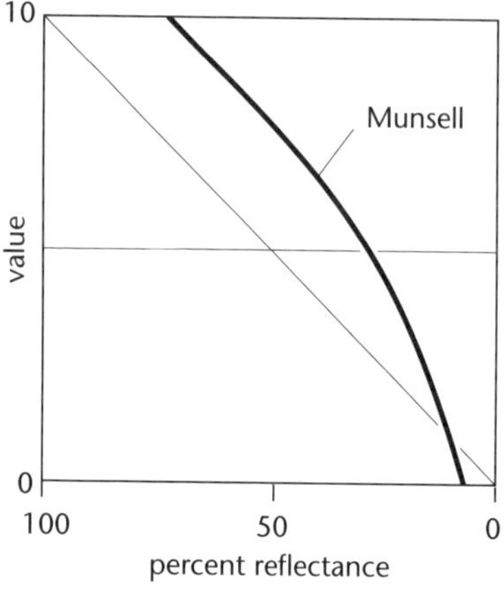


*Figure 5.21* Munsell equal-value gray scale specified in terms of reflectance as derived by Kimerling (1985) for DMA printing paper and ink using 120 lpi dot patterns. The Y-axis represents perceived lightness for the range likely on printed maps which never have pure white paper or zero reflectance from black.

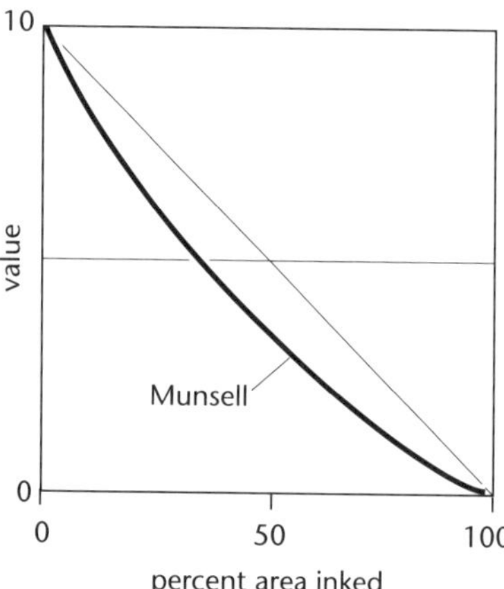


*Figure 5.22* Munsell equal-value gray scale specified in terms of percent area inked as derived by Kimerling (1985). The Y-axis represents perceived lightness for the range likely on printed maps.

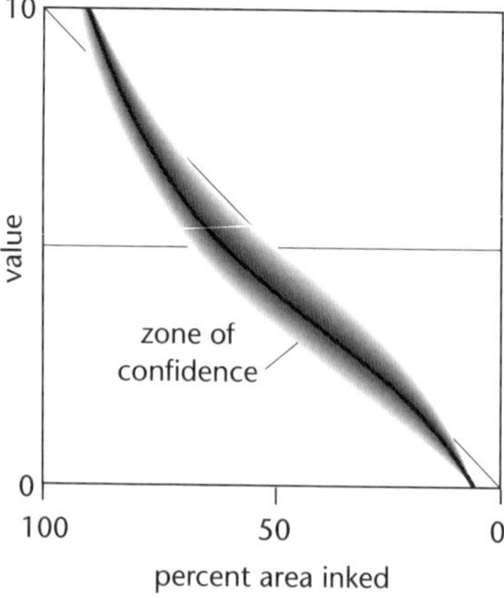


*Figure 5.23* The measured and perceived reflectance relationship empirically determined by Leonard and Buttenfield (1989) and plotted at the same X and Y scale as the Munsell graph above for comparison.

just barely discriminable area fills on the screen to be unreadable in the light end of the range on the printed map, unless gray tones are adjusted before printing.

The second option for using color value to depict data values, one-to-one mapping, is appropriate for exploratory and confirmatory analysis where an analyst usually wants to examine data in as much detail as possible (and for presentation applications where accuracy is a high priority). For this application, using color value in proportion to individual data values will help the analyst identify spatial variation in the information before spatial patterns are confounded or hidden by aggregating the attribute information. This unclassed matching of grays to data values provides the most accurate depiction of the data, but a depiction that is open to many interpretations.

In the case of unclassed maps we can assume that it is perception of darkness or lightness at different points on the map that is important to an analyst (rather than discriminability of pairs of shades as needed for presentation maps). In order to maximize the visualization quality of these unclassed maps, it is again important to recognize that human perception does not judge lightness of an area as a linear function of the percent area inked. For this visual task, however, human perception behaves somewhat differently than it does when faced with the task of judging the relative similarity or difference among a limited set of gray tones. If fine textured (phototypesetter) area fills are used, human perception results in a nearly linear relationship between reflectance and perceived color value (Figure 5.24, page 106). Stevens and Galanter (1957), a team of experimental psychologists, were the first to document this relationship. Based on Kimerling's translation of their results to a percent area inked scale, we can expect 6% area inked to be judged as 20% black, 14% to be judged as 40%, 25% to be judged as 60%, and 46% to be judged as 80% (Figure 5.25, page 106). For the coarser textures of a laser printer map, the curvilinear relationship will be less extreme. Whatever the texture of the area fill, however, if data values are mapped directly to color values, some of the differences at the high end of the data value range will be disguised while those at the low end of the range will be enhanced.

Another issue to be considered in the transfer of computer monitor

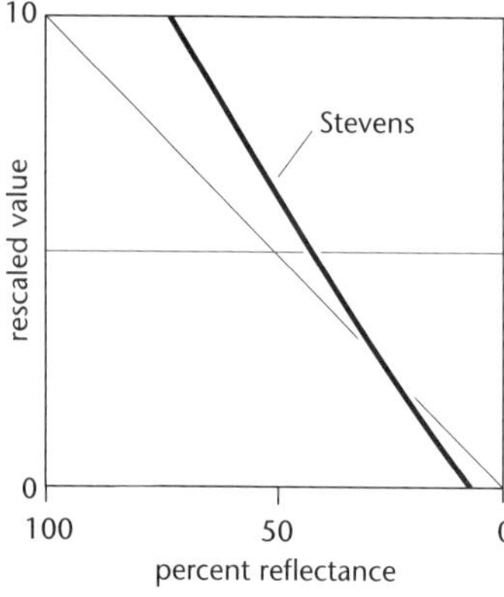


*Figure 5.24* *Stevens equal-value gray scale specified in terms of reflectance as derived by Kimerling (1985) for DMA printing paper and ink using 120 lpi dot patterns. The Y-axis represents perceived lightness for the range likely on printed maps.*

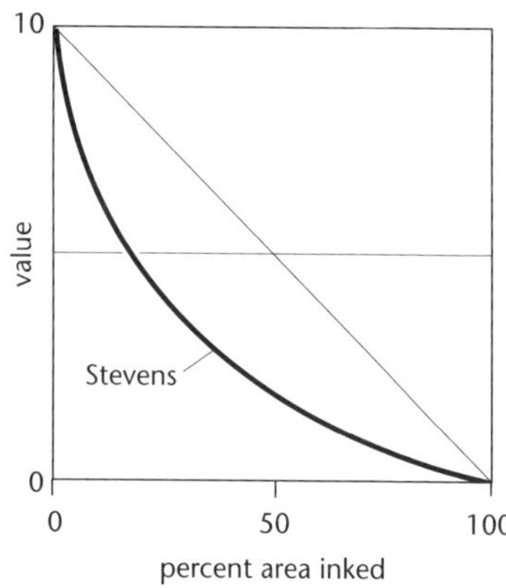


*Figure 5.25* *Stevens equal-value gray scale specified in terms of percent area inked as derived by Kimerling (1985). The Y-axis represents perceived lightness for the range likely on printed maps.*

displays to printed reports is the change in shape and orientation of the display surface (usually from a landscape display with an aspect ratio of 1.33:1 to a portrait display with an aspect ratio of 1:1.38 (if we assume 1" margins on all sides). This change forces either a smaller than maximum scale or printing at an orientation which is at right angles to the text. Usually, space must also be reserved for a caption. If the landscape orientation is retained for easy reading and we retain the computer display aspect ratio, the available space becomes 6.5" x 4.9". The printed display, then, will be about 70% the linear size of its corresponding depiction on the monitor. The higher resolution of the printed page, however, should more than make up for this reduced size. Any details (other than those distinguished by color hue or saturation) that are legible on the monitor will be legible on this half-sized page format.

## Reports—Color Hardcopy

As with the monochrome output described above, color hardcopy devices span a range of resolution from about 150 dpi to over 2000 dpi. Higher resolution allows smaller symbols to be printed but does not necessarily allow smaller differences in color attributes to be noticed. For color value, in fact, coarser area fills are more discriminable. The same is probably true for hue and saturation, (although there has been no cartographic test of this contention). If a report or publication includes color illustrations (either through color photocopy or color printing) we retain the use of all graphic variables, but face some alternative translation issues. Color on computer displays is created by mixtures of red, green, and blue signals, called additive primaries (Figure 5.26). Perceptually, the process is an additive one with the combination of the three primaries emitted at full strength resulting in a white appearance. For printed maps, ink rather than light is mixed (usually as printed overlays). The primary colors used in this case are cyan (a blue-green hue), magenta (a red-blue), and yellow. They are called subtractive primaries because perception of printed color is a function of wavelengths not reflected by the printed page (or "subtracted" from the incident light)( Figure 5.26). In theory at least, the combination of all three subtractive primaries over-printed at 100% results in a black appearance because no light is reflected. In practice a muddy purple or brown usually results. Most color computer printers, therefore, use four rather than three inks with black as the fourth. For either displays (using additive primaries) or prints (using subtractive primaries), a range of hue, value, and saturation combinations can be produced by combining the primaries at different percentages (e.g., 50% cyan + 50% yellow + 0% magenta results in a medium green printed ink). The vagaries of human perception result in imperfect translation between printed color produced by combinations of subtractive primaries and emitted color produced by combinations of additive primaries. It is, thus, rather difficult to match colors seen on a computer screen exactly when they are printed.

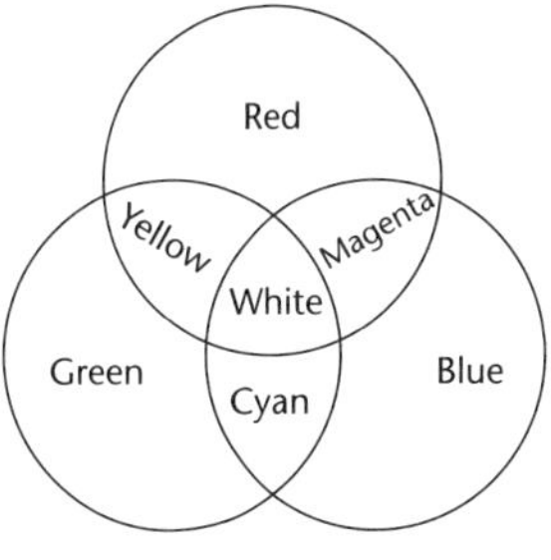

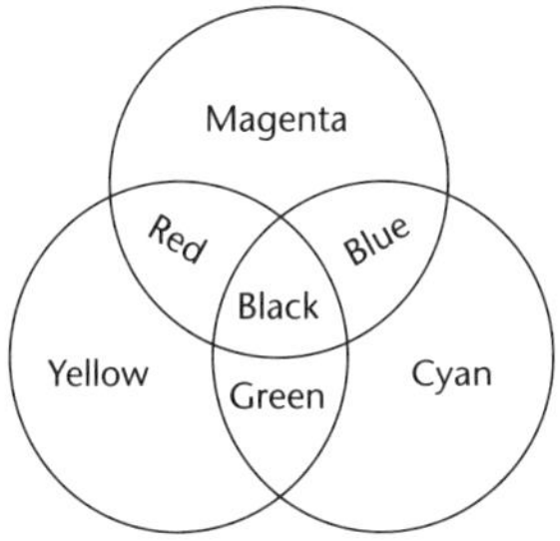


**subtractive primaries**

*Figure 5.26*

The most effective procedure is to create two matched color palettes that can be substituted for one another, one that has color specifications for displayed colors and the other with specifications for printed colors. It is helpful to base these palettes on a single color chart that organizes colors in some logical way. Brown and Schokker (1989) and Brewer (1989) advocate using the Munsell color system because this system is based upon color perception rather than color creation. It, therefore, includes only discriminable colors. The procedure to follow is to begin by selecting a subset of Munsell colors suitable for the range of maps typically produced; then, through trial and error, determine the color specifications (in terms of RGB colors, hue-value-saturation specifications, process colors, Pantone colors, etc.) that result in displayed and printed colors with the closest match to these Munsell colors. For both display and hardcopy, a palette of colors should be created that is keyed to the Munsell chart. Once the palettes exist, map colors can be selected using the "display" palette. Then, when a print is desired, the map maker need only switch to the "hardcopy" palette to change all color specifications to their matching hardcopy values. If swapping of palettes is not possible with the available system, the alternative is to record both display and hardcopy color specifications on the Munsell chart and change colors on an individual basis.

### Presentation Slides

Map design for presentation slides poses rather different problems than generation of color prints for reports. Slides, if made with a digital film recorder, can have much higher resolution than prints made on a thermal printer (and even slightly higher resolution than color separations produced on a phototypesetting machine for production of color printing plates). This implies a potential for more detail in color slides than in other color output. The problem, of course, is that the size at which slides are projected compared with typical viewing distance makes features on slides appear smaller (subtend a smaller angle of vision) than those same features appear on a standard report page. In addition, room lighting during slide presentations and the brightness at which slides can be projected both contribute to difficulties in reading slides. As a result of these issues, slide maps must be less detailed than printed maps if they are to be legible.

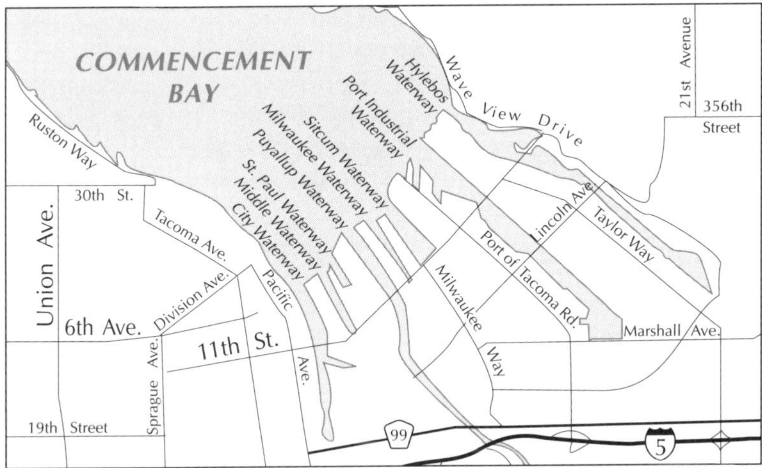


*Figure 5.27 A location map to support toxic chemical analysis of samples taken from Bay sediments. Source: EPA (1991).*

A simple example of a location map will give a feel for the limits of slides. Consider the legibility of Figure 5.27. It is a half-page map with the same aspect ratio as a slide in landscape orientation.[5] All features shown will be legible for most people. The smallest type is 6 point, the smallest type difference is 3 points, the narrowest line feature is 1 point and the smallest difference in line width is 50%. If this slide were viewed on a 7 foot wide screen at a distance of 50 feet (a typical situation in hotel conference rooms) it would look like Figure 5.28. This (approximately) 1:7 ratio of screen width to possible viewing distance, in comparison to the 1:2.8 ratio (6.5" by 18") for the printed page, creates the appearance that the map is only 40% of the original size. Text becomes illegible, and line symbols if they are visible at all, will look the same.

For type on slides to be legible in a typical presentation room, it should be no smaller than 18 points (16 point text would be legible in the exceptional conference room having a 10' screen to 50' depth

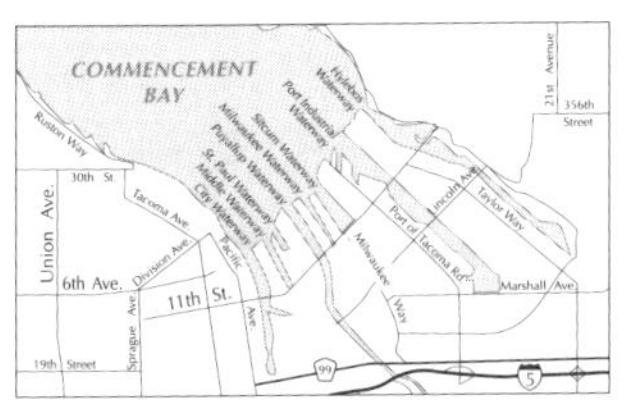

*Figure 5.28 Simulation of the appearance of the Commencement Bay map as depicted in a slide presentation. Source: EPA (1991).*

ratio, but would be hard for most people to read in a typical room). Using similar standards, line features must be at least 1.25 points with 50% differences. Point symbols should also be at least 18 points (0.25 inches) and must have very distinct differences (e.g., a circle versus a triangle or red versus blue rather than a circle versus an asterisk or blue versus green). The relatively large sizes required dictate rather extreme generalization of maps for slides. Figure 5.29 represents the amount of detail that is practical using the recommended text and line sizes.

**Presentation Posters**

If a poster presentation is to be made, the situation is similar to that with slides. Six point lettering viewed at 18" is equivalent to 16 point lettering viewed at 8'. Although 6 point text is legible, it is not comfortable to read (so someone glancing quickly at a poster or peering through a crowd is unlikely to bother reading text at 16 points). Like slides, posters should be interpretable at a glance. Text on posters, then should use at least 20-24 point type. A few details that the particularly interested viewer might come close enough to read can be in 16 point, but you should expect most

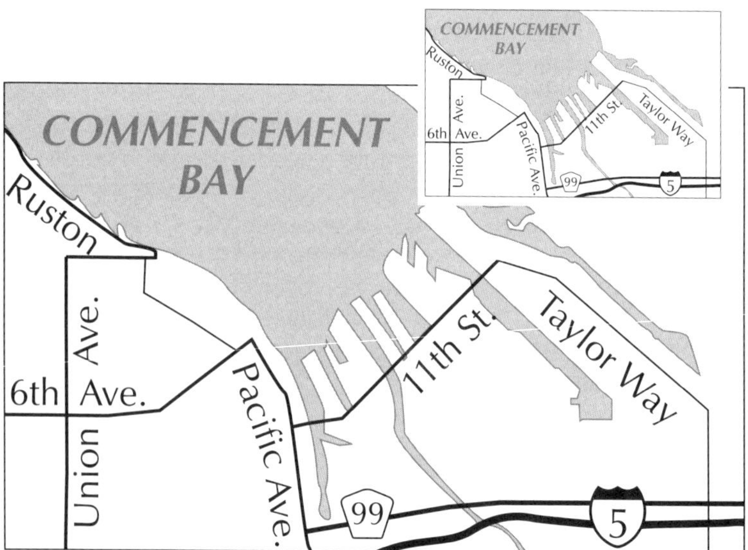


*Figure 5.29 An example of generalization necessary for a legible map slide and, as an inset, what the slide would look like from the back of a conference room. Source: EPA (1991).*

viewers to skip these details. For linear features, 1 point line widths should be the minimum with at least 50% difference in width. Point symbols should be no smaller than 18 point (0.25 inches) and, again, should have distinct differences if the differences are to be legible at a distance.

## Video

Dynamic maps seen directly on a computer monitor offer tremendous potential for exploratory analysis in environmental science and other earth science applications. Videotape is currently the most accessible medium for presenting the results of dynamic analysis (although the optical disk may supplant it by the end of the decade). Videotape is a relatively new medium for environmental maps. Although animated maps on film have been created from time to time for several decades, and television news and weather reports have employed dynamic maps with increasing frequency, maps for environmental research or policy making have seldom been produced in this form. What has become clear from other map applications of video is that videotape poses a number of unique cartographic problems.

Most obvious among the issues that must be addressed when producing a dynamic map to be recorded on video tape is how to make best use of the new graphic variable — time. DiBiase, et al. (1992) have dealt with this issue in detail. They suggest that viewing–time can be used symbolically to depict existence of features, attributes of features, and change in existence or attributes. Within change, they identify three categories, change in position of viewer, change in location of attributes or attributes at locations, and reexpression (use of time to represent an ordered variable other than time). Viewing-time, then, can represent actual time (as map space represents geographic space) or it can act as a graphic variable with, for example, duration of symbol appearance depicting magnitude of toxic spills (as space in a cartogram is used to portray something other than geographic space).

Along with the potential of a dynamic map to explicate dynamic processes (or simply catch the viewer's attention) comes a number of limitations of the medium of videotape. Television monitors are analog rather than digital devices that have relatively low resolution and somewhat fuzzy images compared to a computer monitor.

As a result, all features must be slightly enlarged and more generalized than for display directly on the computer monitor. In addition, most conference or public meeting rooms have rather poor video presentation systems (usually consisting of a regular sized television screen viewed from considerable distance). A two foot wide television screen at twenty feet, for example, produces a viewing ratio of 1:10, considerably worse than for slides. Together with the fact that television resolution is much less than slide resolution, you cannot expect any text smaller than about 24 point to be legible. If viewed from 50 feet, text on a television monitor would need to be 60 point! In addition to the size and resolution constraints, U.S. NTSC standards for broadcast video restrict the allowable saturation of most color hues because highly saturated colors tend to smear across the screen. This limitation in saturation is greatest for reds and yellows, two hues that are particularly desireable on maps of environmental risk.

## Summary

This chapter has touched on a few key issues in planning map composition in a spatial analysis/decision support context. Central to this planning is the establishment of geographic hierarchies and geographic context. Both are considered in relation to the potential for manipulating map design so that viewer attention is directed toward specific features and relationships. In addition, the role of marginal information in enhancing visualization quality by removing ambiguity and the potential for misunderstanding is addressed. Finally, the variety of display media that are used and the problems encountered when shifting from virtual (computer monitor) maps to hardcopy are considered and guidelines for changing among media are provided.

### Endnotes

[1]*Cynthia Brewer (1992 and in press) has developed a comprehensive strategy for color assignment in the context of geographic data analysis and visualization. Her system begins with a taxonomy of mapping situations to which color can be applied. This taxonomy is based on a distinction among qualitative, sequential (unidirectional) quantitative, and divergent (bidirectional) quantitative data as the major data types. Brewer considers color assignment to each of these types individually and to their paired combinations. The most complex situation, then, is when two bidirectional (double-ended) quantitative data ranges are combined on the same map. Readers are encouraged to consult Brewer (in press) for a more comprehensive look at color on multivariate maps.*

[2]*See Monmonier (1993) for further suggestions on titles and other labels.*

[3]*The abbreviation dpi stands for dots per inch and refers to the resolution at which a raster display or output device can print. Any pattern printed or displayed on a raster device must be constructed by combining adjacent dots. Texture of patterns thus generated are specified in lines per inch (lpi). When patterns represent a range of gray tones, their lpi can be no finer than about 1/4 of the device resolution.*

[4]*Leonard and Buttenfield's (1989) results have not been converted to percent–area–inked terms; therefore, they are a bit hard to apply. For the 42 line per inch patterns used, however, the relationship between percent reflectance and percent area inked will be marginally non–linear resulting in slightly more difference needed among dark grays and slightly less among light grays (if they are specified as percent area inked).*

[5]*It is impractical in most places to use portrait orientation slides because most screens have a landscape orientation. Having even one portrait slide in your presentation, then, can force all slides to be viewed at reduced size so that the portrait slides fit on the screen (or will force you to constantly readjust size if you have a zoom lens on the projector).*

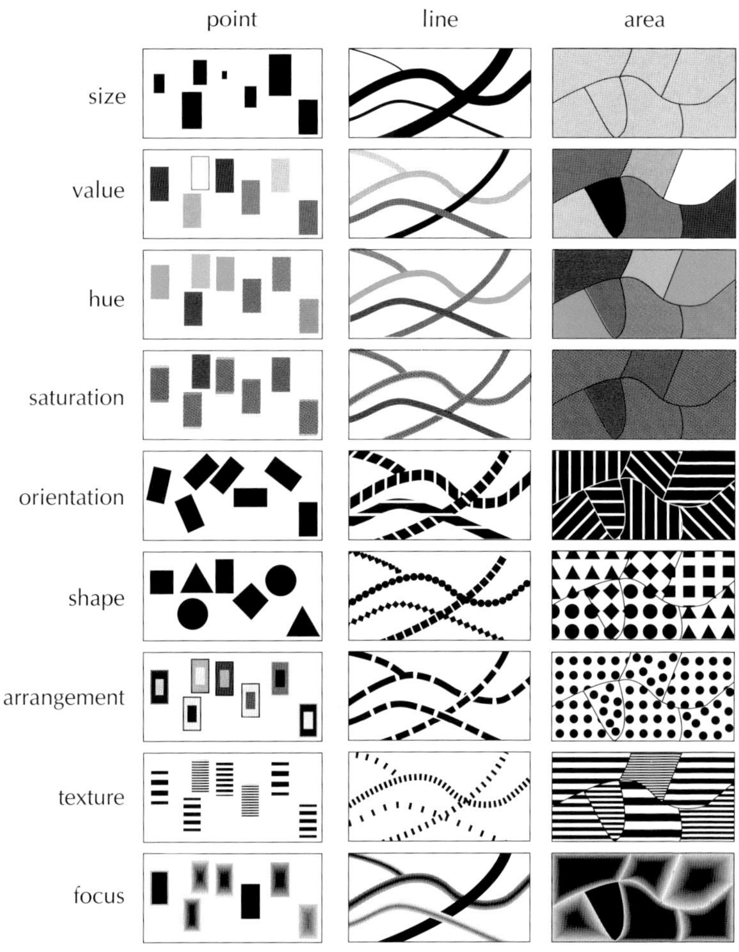
point
line
area
size
value
hue
saturation
orientation
shape
arrangement
texture
focus

*Figure C2.04*

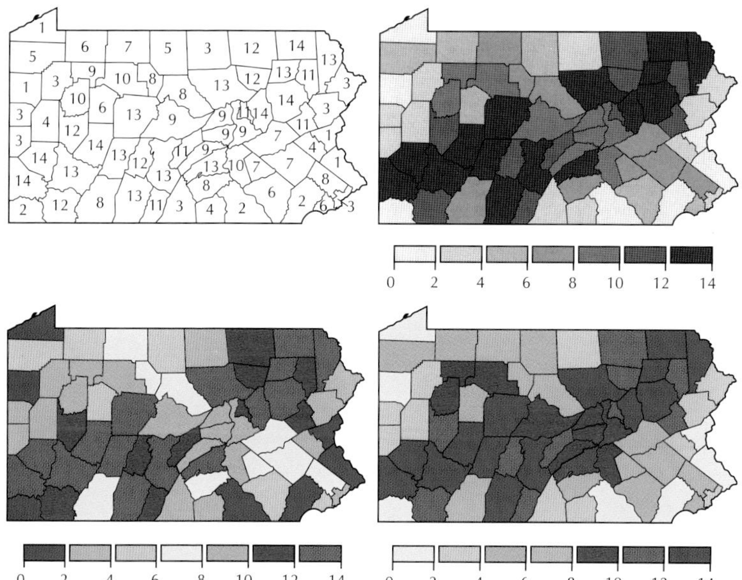


*Figure C 2.14*

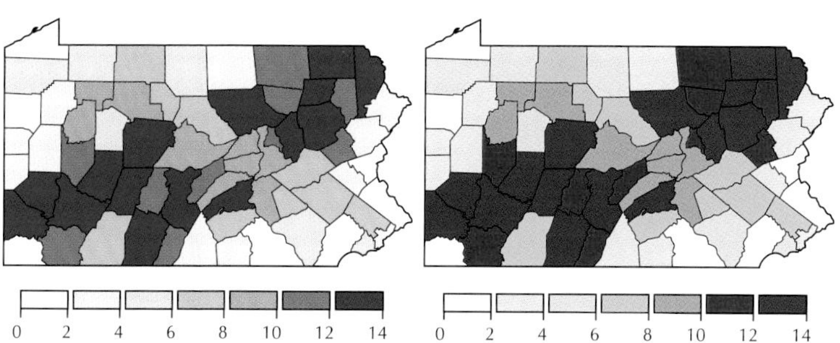


*Figure C2.15*

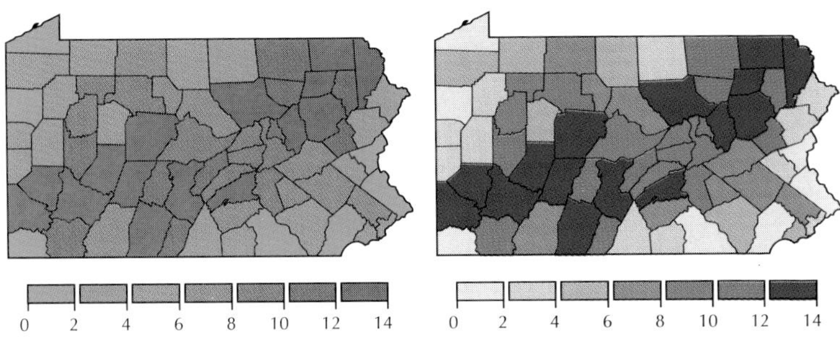


*Figure C2.17*

*Figure C2.18*

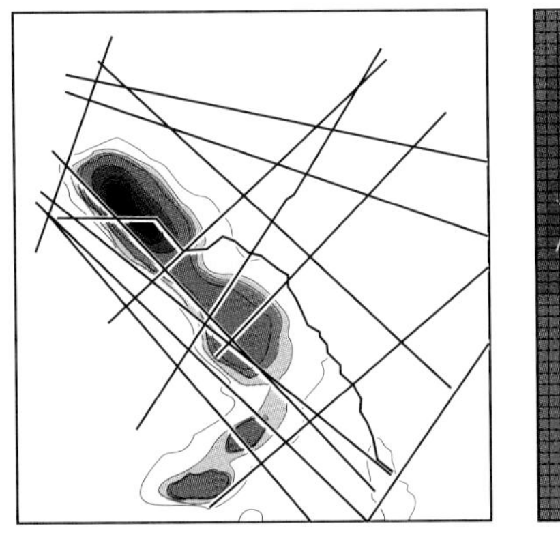

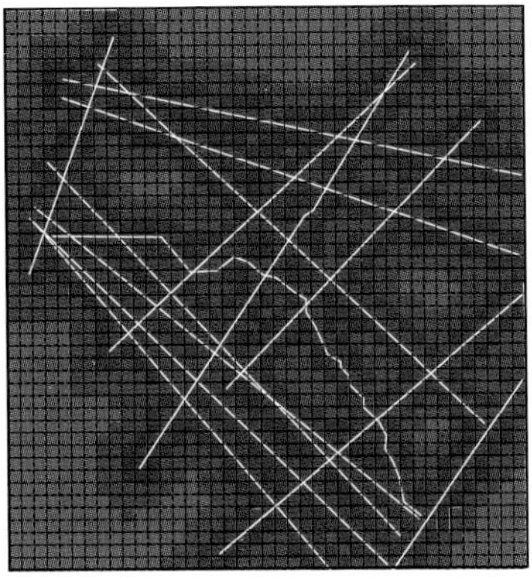

*Figure C4.09*

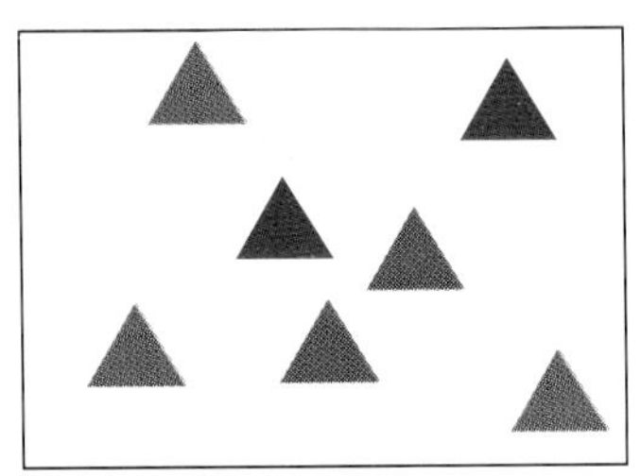

*Figure C4.10*

**INCIDENCE OF CANCER OF THE TRACHEA, BRONCHUS, LUNG AND PLEURA, 1986**

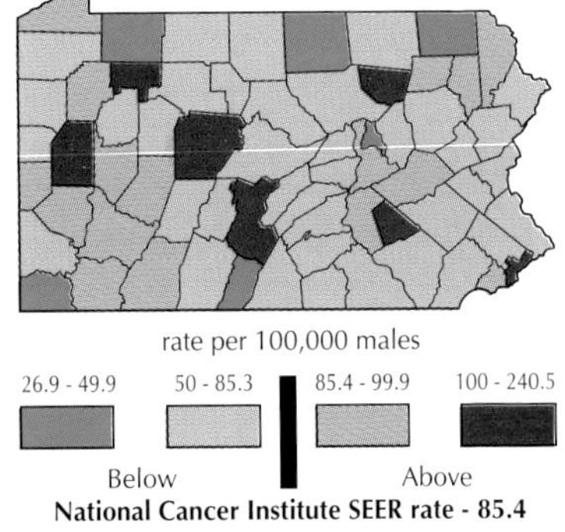


*Figure C5.08*

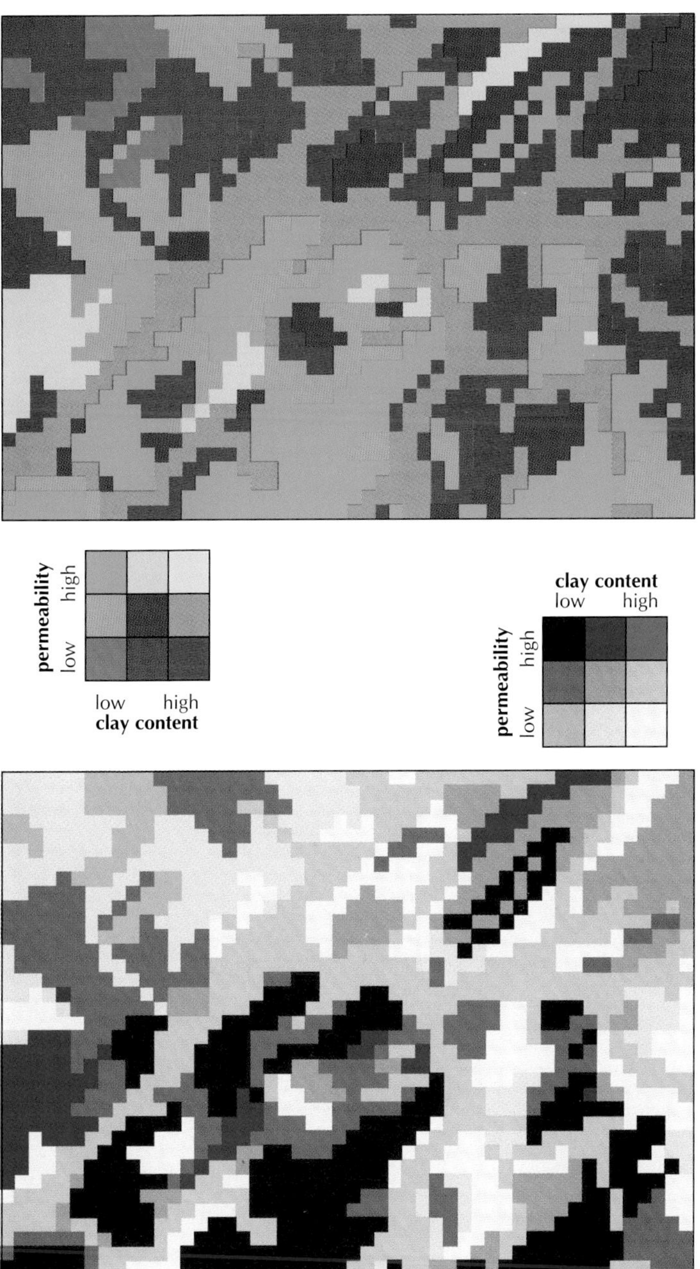
permeability
high
low
low
high
clay content
clay content
low
high
permeability
high
low

*Figure C5.10*

## Postscript

Of necessity, this Resource Paper leaves out as many issues about map symbolization and design as it covers. The goal, however, was not to provide a comprehensive text. Some of the more useful of these are listed in the Bibliography and in the Suggestions for Additional Reading. The reader is encouraged to consult them. Rather than providing comprehensive coverage, this resource paper portrays a process for map design and symbolization that is suited to a range of map uses from exploratory to presentational. The principal objective has been to direct attention to a few critical issues faced by those using maps as both problem investigation and solution presentation tools, and to put these issues into a logical context.

If we are to take advantage of the power that computer mapping tools and GIS provide to deal with space, time, and attributes together rather than separately, we will have to learn to take better advantage of our human skills at visual analysis. The massive amounts of information now at our finger tips can not be analyzed by traditional means. Having access to maps, graphics, statistics, images, etc. in a system that allows us to flexibly integrate the information in almost unlimited ways opens new possibilities for understanding our environment and the natural and human induced risks associated with it. To use visualization tools effectively with GIS demands that we examine procedures of their use as carefully as we have examined the rules for statistical analysis in the past. My hope is that this Resource Paper will be a step toward building better analysis and policy formulation tools for dealing with complex geographic problems.

## Bibliography


**ACSM Committee on Map Projections.** 1988. *Choosing a world map.* Falls Church, VA: American Congress on Surveying and Mapping.

**ACSM Committee on Map Projections.** 1991. *Matching the map projection to the need.* Falls Church, VA: American Congress on Surveying and Mapping.

**Beard, M. K., and Buttenfield, B. P.** 1991. *NCGIA research initiative 7: Visualization of spatial data quality,* NCGIA, Technical Paper: (91-26).

**Bertin, J.** 1981. *Graphics and graphic information processing.* Berlin: Walter de Gruyter.

**Bertin, J.** 1983. *Semiology of graphics: Diagrams, networks, maps.* Madison, WI: University of Wisconsin Press.

**Brewer, C.A.** 1989. The development of process-printed Munsell charts for selecting map colors. *American Cartographer* 16(4): 269-78.

__________. 1992. Color selection for geographic data analysis and visualization. Paper presented at GIS/LIS, November, 12, 1992. San Jose, CA.

__________. 1993. *Color selection for maps: Interactive tutorial,* San Jose, CA: avialable from author, (hypermedia document).

__________. in press. Color use guidelines for mapping and visualization. In *Visualization in modern cartography,* ed. A. M. MacEachren and D. R. F. Taylor, London: Pergamon.

**Brown, A., and van Elzakker, C. P. J. M.** 1993. The use of colour in the cartographic representation of information quality generated by a GIS. *Proceedings, 16th International Cartographic Conference* May 3-9, 1993, Cologne, Germany, pp. 707-20.

**Brown, A. M. A., and Schokker, P. W. M.** 1989. The design and production of an offset printed colour chart for use with a graphic artwork program on the Macintosh II microcomputer. Paper presented at the 14 Meeting of the International Cartographic Association. Budapest, Hungary, (manuscript).

**Buttenfield, B. P.**, Ed. in press. *Mapping data quality, Cartographica,* Monograph.

**DeLucia, A. A., and Hiller, D. W.** 1982. Natural legend design for thematic maps. *Cartographic Journal* 19: 46-52.

**DiBiase, D.** 1990. Visualization in the earth sciences. *Earth and Mineral Sciences,* Bulletin of the College of Earth and Mineral Sciences, PSU 59(2): 13-18.

__________. 1991. Personal communication.

**DiBiase, D.; Krygier, J. B.; Reeves, C.; MacEachren, A. M.; and Brenner, A.** 1991. *An Elementary Approach to Cartographic Animation,* University Park, PA: Deasy GeoGraphics Laboratory, Dept. of Geog., Penn State, (video).

**DiBiase, D.; MacEachren, A. M.; Krygier, J. B.; and Reeves, C.** 1992. Animation and the role of map design in scientific visualization. *Cartography and Geographic Information Systems* 19(4): 201-14.

**EPA** (U.S. Environmental Protection Agency) 1990a. *GIS program phase II study: The Pennsylvania project,* EPA Region III, Ground Water Protection Section, Philadelphia, PA.

__________. 1990b. *Region 6 comparative risk project, Appendix A: Ecological Report,* EPA Region 6 Office of Planning and Analysis, Dallas, TX.

__________. 1991. Project maps, Office of Research and Development, Environmental Monitoring Systems Laboratory–Las Vegas.

**Evans, I. S.** 1977. The selection of class intervals. *Transactions of the Institute of British Geographers New series* 2: 98-124.

**Ferreia, J., and Wiggins, L.** 1990. The density dial: A visualization tool for thematic mapping. *GeoInfo Systems* 1: 69-71.

**Fothergill, S., and Vincent, J.** 1985. *The state of the nation: An atlas of Britain in the eighties.* London: Pan Books, Ltd.

**Gould, P.** 1989. Geographic dimensions of the AIDS epidemic. *The Professional Geographer* 41(1): 71-78.

__________. 1993. *The slow plague: A geography of the AIDS pandemic.* Cambridge, Mass.: Blackwell.

**Gould, P.; DiBiase, D.; and Kabel, J.** 1990. Le SIDA: la carte animée comme rhetorique cartographique appliquée. *Mappe Monde* 90(1): 21-26.

**Gould, P.; Kabel, J.; Gorr, W.; and Golub, A.** 1991. AIDS: Predicting the next map. *Interfaces* 21(3): 80-92.

**Groop, E.** 1980. *An optimal data classifications program for choropleth mapping,* Technical Report No. 3, Department of Geography, Michigan State University.

**Harley, J. B.** 1989. Deconstructing the map. *Cartographica* 26(2): 1-20.

**Head, C.G.** 1984. The map as a natural language: A paradigm for understanding. *Cartographica,* Monograph 31, 21(1): 1-32.

**Hsu, M.-L.** 1979. The cartographer's conceptual process and thematic symbolization. *American Cartographer* 6: 117-27.

**Hubel, D. H.** 1988. *Eye, brain and vision.* New York: Scientific American Library, distributed by W. H. Freeman.

**Hutzler, E., and Spiess, E.** 1993. A knowledge-based thematic mapping system - the other way round. *Proceedings, 16th International Cartographic Conference* Cologne, Germany, May 3-9, 1993, pp. 329-40.

**Jenks, G. F.** 1967. The data model concept in statistical mapping. *International Yearbook of Cartography* 7: 186-90.

________. 1977. Optimal data classification for choropleth maps. Occasional Paper No. 2, Department of Geography, University of Kansas.

**Keates, J. S.** 1982. *Understanding maps.* New York: Halsted Press (division of John Wiley & Sons).

**Kimerling, A. J.** 1985. The comparison of equal-value gray scales. *American Cartographer* 12: 132-42.

**Kraak, M.-J.** 1988. *Computer-assisted cartographical three dimensional imaging techniques.* Delft: The Netherlands: Delft University Press.

**Krygier, J.** in press. Sound and geographic visualization. In *Visualization in modern cartography.* ed. A. M. MacEachren, and D. R.F. Taylor. Oxford, UK: Pergamon.

**Langford, M., and Unwin, D.J.** 1991. Generating and mapping population density surfaces within a geographical information system (manuscript).

**Leonard, J. J., and Buttenfield, B. P.** 1989. An equal value gray scale for laser printer mapping. *American Cartographer* 16(2): 97-107.

**Liverman, D. M., and O'Brien, K. L.** 1991. Global warming and climate change in Mexico. *Global Environmental Change* 1(4): 351-64.

**MacDougall, E.B.** 1992. Exploratory Analysis, Dynamic Statistical Visualization, and Geographic Information Systems. *Cartography and Geographic Information Systems* 19(4): 237-46.

**MacEachren, A. M.,** 1992. Visualizing uncertain information. *Cartographic Perspectives* (13): 10-19.

**MacEachren, A. M.**, (in collaboration with, Buttenfield, B., Campbell, J., DiBiase, D. and Monmonier, M. ). 1992. Visualization. In *Geography's inner worlds: Pervasive themes in contemporary American Geography*, ed. R. Abler, M. Marcus and J. Olson, pp. 99-137. New Brunswick, NJ: Rutgers University Press.

**MacEachren, A. M., and Davidson, J. V.** 1987. Sampling and isometric mapping of continuous geographic surfaces. *The American Cartographer* 14(4): 299-320.

**MacEachren, A. M., and DiBiase, D. W.** 1991. Animated maps of aggregate data: Conceptual and practical problems. *Cartography and Geographic Information Systems* 18(4): 221-29.

**MacEachren, A. M., and Ganter, J. H.** 1990. A pattern identification approach to cartographic visualization. *Cartographica* 27(2): 64-81.

**MacEachren, A. M.; Howard, D.; von Wyss, M.; Askov, D.; and Taormino, T.** 1993. *Visualizing the health of Chesapeake Bay: An uncertain endeavor, Proceedings, GIS/LIS'93* Minneapolis, Nov. 2-4, 449-458.

**MacEachren, A. M., and Mistrick, T. A.** 1992. The role of brightness differences in figure-ground: is darker figure? *Cartographic Journal* 29(2): 91-100.

**McCleary, G. F.** 1983. An effective graphic 'vocabulary'. *IEEE Computer Graphics & Applications* March: 46-53.

**McGranaghan, M.** 1989. Ordering choropleth map symbols: The effect of background. *American Cartographer* 16(4): 279-85.

**McLay, W. J.** 1987. *Two-variable mapping: A practical case for the soil map,* unpublished Master's Thesis, The Pennsylvania State University.

**Merriam-Webster** 1974. 'precision'. In *Webster's new collegiate dictionary,* pp. 905. Springfield, Mass.: G. & C. Merriam Company.

**Moellering, H.** 1989. A practical and efficient approach to the stereoscopic display and manipulation of cartographic objects. *Proceedings, Auto-Carto 9* Baltimore, pp. 1-4.

**Monmonier, M**. 1991a. *How to lie with maps.* Chicago: University of Chicago Press.

__________. 1991b. Ethics and map design: Six strategies for confronting the traditional one-map solution. *Cartographic Perspectives* 10: 3-8.

**Monmonier, M.** 1993. *Mapping it out: Expository cartography for the humanities and social sciences*. Chicago: University of Chicago Press.

**Monmonier, M., and Johnson, B., B.** 1990. *Design guide for environmental maps,* New Jersey Department of Environmental Protection, Division of Social Science, Trenton, NJ.

**Morgan, M. G., and Henrion, M.** 1990. The graphic communication of uncertainty, chapter 9. In *Uncertainty: A guide to dealing with uncertainty in quantitative risk and policy analysis,* pp. 220-56. Cambridge: Cambridge University Press.

**Morrison, J. L.** 1984. Applied cartographic communication: Map symbolization for atlases. In *New insights in cartographic communication, Cartographica Monograph 31,* ed. C. Board, pp. 44-84.

**Muehrcke, P.** 1990. Cartography and geographic information systems. *Cartography and Geographic Information Systems* 17(1): 7-15.

**Muller, J.-C., and Zeshen, W.** 1990. A knowledge based system for cartographic symbol design. *Cartographic Journal* 27: 24-30.

**Olson, J. M.** 1981. Spectrally encoded two-variable maps. *Annals of the Association of American Geographers* 71(2): 259-76.

**Omernik, J.M.** 1982. Total alkalinity of surface waters, map published by the Corvallis Environmental Research Laboratory, U.S. Environmental Protection Agency.

**Omernik, J. M., and Powers, C. F.** 1983. Total alkalinity of surface waters - A national map (with map supplement). *Annals of the Association of American Geographers* 73(1): 133-66.

**Pennsylvania Emergency Management Agency.** 1990. *Action report, Ashland oil spill, January 2, 1988.*

**Pennsylvania Department of Health.** 1990. *Cancer incidence and mortality in Pennsylvania, 1986.*

**Rahn, K. A.** 1982. On the causes, characteristics and potential environmental effects of aerosol in the arctic atmosphere. In *The Acrtic Ocean: The hydrographic environment and the fate of pollutants,* ed. L. Rey, pp. 163-95. New York: Wiley.

**Rejeski, D., and Kapuscinski, J.** 1990. *Risk modeling with geographic information systems: Approaches and issues,* U. S. Environmental Protection Agency, Office of Information Resources Management.

**Schlichtmann, H.** 1985. Characteristic traits of the semiotic system 'map symbolism'. *The Cartographic Journal* 22: 23-30.
**Stevens, S. S., and Galanter, E. H.** 1957. Ratio scales and category scales for a dozen perceptual continua. *Journal of Experimental Psychology* 54: 377-411.
**Tobler, W.R.** 1973. Choropleth maps without class intervals. *Geographical Analysis* 5: 262-65.
**van der Wel, F.J.M.** 1993. Visualization of quality informations as an indispensable part of optimal information extraction from a GIS. *Proceedings, 16th International Cartographic Conference* May 3-9, 1993, Cologne, Germany, pp. 881-97.
**Vasconcellos, R.** 1993. Representing the geographical space for visually handicapped students: A case study on map use. *Proceedings, 16th International Cartographic Conference* May 3-9, 1993, Cologne, Germany, pp. 993-1004.
**Weibel, R., and Buttenfield, B. P.** 1988. Map design for geographic information systems. *Proceedings, GIS/LIS'88* San Antonio, TX, pp. 350-59.
**Wilmont, J. C.; Rowe, C. M.; and Philpot, W. D.** 1985. Small-scale climate maps: A sensitivity analysis of some common assumptions associated with grid-point interpolation and contouring. *The American Cartographer* 12(1): 5-16.
**Wood, D.** 1992. *The power of maps.* New York: The Guilford Press.
**Yarnal, B., and Diaz, H. F.** 1986. Relationships between extremes of the sourthern oscillation and the winter climate of the AngloAmerican Pacific coast. *Journal of Climatology* 6: 197-219.

## Suggestions for Additional Reading

**Anson, R. W.**, Ed. 1984. *Basic cartography for students and technicians, Vol. 2.* International Cartographic Association, Commission on Education in Cartography.
**Dent, B. D.** 1993. *Cartography: Thematic map design.* 3rd ed. Dubuque, Iowa: Wm. C. Brown Publishers.
**Fisher, H. T.** 1982. *Mapping information: The graphic display of quantitative information.* Cambridge, Mass.: Abt Books.
**ICA Commission on Education in Cartography.** 1984. *Basic cartography for students and technicians, Vol. 1.* International Cartographic Association.

**Keates, J. S.** 1989. *Cartographic design and production*. New York: Wiley.

**McCleary, G. F.** 1981. How to design an effective graphics presentation. In *Harvard Library of Computer Graphics 1981 Mapping Collection*, pp. 15-64.

**McMaster, R. B., and Shea, K. S.** 1992. *Generalization in digital cartography*. Washington, DC: Association of American Geographers.

**Muehrcke, P.** 1992. *Map use: Reading, analysis, and interpretation*. 3rd ed. Madison, WI: JP Publications.

**Szegö, J.** 1987. *Human cartography: Mapping the world of man*. Stockholm: Swedish Council for Building Research.

**Taylor, D. R. F.**, Ed. 1991. *Geographic information systems: The microcomputer and modern cartography*. Oxford, UK: Pergamon.

**Tufte, E.** 1983. *The visual display of quantitative information*. Cheshire, Conn.: Graphics Press.

**Tufte, E.** 1990. *Envisioning information*. Cheshire, Conn.: Graphics Press.